Farming

SOURCES FOR LOCAL HISTORIANS

Farming

SOURCES FOR LOCAL HISTORIANS

Peter Edwards

B. T. Batsford Ltd · London

Typeset by Deltatype Ltd, Ellesmere Port

and printed in Great Britain
by Dotesios Ltd Trowbridge, Wilts

for the publishers
B. T. Batsford Ltd
4 Fitzhardinge Street
London W1H 0AH

A catalogue record for this book
is available from the British Library

ISBN 0 7134 5116 5

CONTENTS

LIST OF PLATES

corn. In this photograph, taken on 5 December 1940, a plough team is seen at work at Troutbeck in the Lake District, preparing the ground for a spring sowing of oats.

8   *Mechanization on the farm (1)*: a tractor engine pulling a plough on a Berkshire farm

9   *Mechanization on the farm (2)* cutting the hay on a farm near Wincanton, (Somerset) *c.*1900. The horse-drawn device was known as a Trapper mowing machine.

10   *Farm labour (1)*: male and female farm labourers reaping and binding corn on a Staffordshire farm in the late nineteenth century.

11   *Farm labour (2)*: threshing provided farm labourers with a valuable source of income during the winter months and for this reason many of them opposed the introduction of threshing machines. It was an extremely arduous task, however, and when alternative winter work became available labourers willingly gave it up.

12   *Bringing in the harvest (1)*: men and women at work in the field in the Henley-on-Thames area, mowing the hay and loading into horesdrawn wagons.

13   *Bringing in the harvest (2)*: hop picking at Cranbrook, Kent, an example of a regional agricultural specialization. Here, at the turn of the nineteenth century, oxen were still being used to pull the waggons.

14   *Employment of Children on the farm*: children carting off the corn on a Sussex farm. In rural districts many schools until comparatively recent times found themselves denuded of pupils at harvest time as the children helped on the farm.

15   *The Marketing of Livestock*: view of the old livestock market in North Street, Guildford (Surrey), showing tethered cattle and penned sheep. In 1895 the market was moved out of the town centre to Woodbridge Road.

Acknowledgements

I am grateful to the following for giving me permission to reproduce the whole or part of documents in their possession:

Appendix 1: Surrey Record Office; Appendix 2: Shropshire Record Office; Appendix 3: Mr M. Willoughby; Appendix 4: Wolverhampton Boys' Grammar School; Appendix 5: The Earl of Shrewsbury; Appendix 6: The Lichfield Diocesan Registrar; Appendix 7: Crown Copyright, Public Record Office; Appendix 8: Somerset Record Office.

I am grateful to the following for permission to publish their material: Shropshire Record Office for the maps of Longford and Church Aston, Ref. SRO 81/599; Warwickshire Record Office for the map of Atherstone; Ref. Atherstone Strip Map 1716 P7.

INTRODUCTION

Many people, having become interested in the history of their own community, will wish to extend their knowledge of it by looking at particular topics in greater detail. The development of local farming practices is a good place for them to start. Even if they live in towns, suburbs or commuter villages, having little or no connection with the land, in the past many of these places, or at least the fields on which the houses were built, were more closely associated with farming. Indeed, before the late eighteenth century when the rate of industrial development accelerated, agriculture was by far the most important sector of the economy. In absolute terms, moreover, the numbers involved continued to increase until the mid nineteenth century.

Clearly, farming practices over the centuries have had a tremendous influence on the social and economic life of the country, and many of the major themes will be dealt with during the course of this book. Local historians should, of course, be aware of general developments in agriculture and are therefore advised to familiarize themselves with overall trends so that they fit their work into its proper context. The parish of Great Bookham in Surrey, for instance, is an interesting place for me to study not only because it is the village in which I live but also because it shares many characteristics with other downland communities elsewhere in England. An appreciation of the wider issues gives a local investigation a sense of direction, raising questions and providing hypotheses which can be tested against the local source material.

To acquire the essential background information readers should consult an up-to-date general text book on agriculture.[1] Moreover, they should look at specialist journals like the *Agricultural History Review* for points of general application, as well as for those articles which have a local or regional basis. Closer to home, the journals of local history societies and the transactions of the county historical and archaeological society will contain material of local interest.

Before examining original manuscripts researchers should read all the relevant material which has appeared in print. Local historical journals often include transcripts of documents, as well as articles, whilst the publications of the county record society give a more extended coverage of source material. Their value is enhanced if properly indexed and provided with a detailed introduction (which might even contain an analysis of the documentation). Old histories of the parish might also help, as many include extracts from documents. Uvedale Lambert's work on the history of Bletchingley (Surrey) is a good example of this point.[2] The volumes of the Historical Manuscript Commission with their surveys of collections of documents should be consulted as well. In the past, much information in private hands was available to local historians only through these volumes, and they are still of use today in spite of the growth in the number of record offices and the greater accessibility of archival collections. Apart from acting as a guide to the contents of the archive, they may provide sufficient detail to make it unnecessary to look at the original.

Often the printed text is given in the form of calendars, that is, abstracts of information contained in the original. Deeds of various sorts have often been processed in this way, the common form of much of the content making them easy to abridge. Record offices have calendars of deeds in their possession (and copies of calendars of local documents held elsewhere), though the number varies according to the pressure of work on individual archivists and the competing calls on their time. On a national scale the Public Record Office (PRO) has calendared many of its deeds, and this work has been continued by the List and Index Society. Other local references appear in calendars of the records of central government, in such publications as the Calendar of State Papers. These volumes are available locally but tend to be restricted to universities and large libraries.

Stress in the past has been laid on the transcription, calendaring and indexing of medieval records. This is particularly noticeable in the work of the nineteenth-century Record Commissioners who calendared vast amounts of early material deposited in the PRO, but it has also been a priority task of county archivists too. Thus, medieval deeds will often have been thoroughly calendared, whilst later ones, where listed, may have had merely the basic information taken from them – the date and identification of the document, together with the names, addresses and statuses of the parties concerned.

Sooner or later, however, manuscript sources have to be examined and these can present the non-specialist with a number of difficulties. The first one is access to the material. The subject of the study may be an aspect of local history but the documents are often located at a distance. In particular, many records have been moved to county or diocesan record offices (the two are often the same). There, of course, they can be kept properly and, if necessary, be repaired. Researchers also benefit from having a range of sources in one place, a facility which is further enhanced if the material has been indexed and calendared. The record office, however, may be a number of miles away and open only during the daytime (though many do have evening and Saturday sessions). Moreover, whilst local historians living in a village which formed part of a large estate, have an undoubted advantage over others, they may have to pay for it in time and travel expenses. Estate records are normally found in either the estate muniment room or the record office of the county where the big house is located. Because of the scattered nature of many estates, the material could be stored at the other end of the country. This is a real possibility for local historians whose communities are on the Crown estate (or had at one time been part of it). Generally speaking, these records have been deposited in the PRO in Chancery Lane, London, though the archives of the Duchy of Cornwall, for instance, are available 'locally'. To discover if one's own community is affected (and Crown lands in the past were even more extensive than they are today) the best source of reference is the relevant topographical volume of the *Victoria County Histories of England*. In the manorial section of each parish account the descent of all the manors covered by it are given, often in considerable detail. Other valuable sources of information are to be found in the national archives. It is therefore perhaps not surprising to learn that in many quarters local history is still seen as a retirement pursuit!

The documents themselves will present the non-specialist with other problems. Medieval manuscripts are not only difficult to read but are also usually written in Latin or occasionally in Norman French. For those with no knowledge of the language or at best a hazy recollection of what was learned at school, this may appear an insurmountable obstacle. In such circumstances it would be tempting to stick to printed material or to go no further back than the mid sixteenth century, covering a period when it is possible to write a reasonable account of local farming without looking at sources written in Latin. This would be a mistake. Firstly, valuable information would have to be ignored: many deeds, quarter sessions' records and manor court rolls continued to be written in Latin until 1733 (with the exception of the Commonwealth period 1653–60). Secondly, the task of translation is not as daunting as it seems, for the Latin of the documents is less complex than that of the classical period. Scribes not only thought in English, constructing their sentences in a manner more akin to their native language, but they also employed a more limited vocabulary, repeatedly using stock words and phrases. Of course, some classes of documentation are more easy to read then others: medieval account rolls, for instance, with their standard format and greater legibility, are easier to use than manor court rolls. For guidance, readers should have access to C. T. Martin's *The Record Interpreter* (Stevens & Sons, London 1949) which contains a list of abbreviations and Latin words and names, and a dictionary like R. E. Latham's *Revised Medieval Latin Word-List* (British Academy, London, 1965). For questions of grammar they should use E. A. Gooder's *Latin for Local History: An Introduction* (Longmans, London, 1978).

Local historians, however, cannot plunge straight into medieval documents and hope immediately to understand what they say. The style of writing is strange – the letters look different and the words are often heavily contracted. The non-specialist should, therefore, start with more modern material, gradually working backwards through the documentation. The form of writing on documents dating from about 1700 is recognizably modern, but, although earlier records are more difficult to decipher, change did not occur overnight. Archaic lettering will often appear in a context which makes clear the meaning of the word and this aids comprehension. With help from guides such as H. E. P. Grieve's *Examples of English Handwriting 1150–1750* (Essex Record Office Publication, no. 21, Chelmsford, 1954) readers should be able to transcribe documents as early as the mid sixteenth century when the 'secretary hand' was introduced. Earlier scripts present more of a problem, but by then experience gained in reading later hands will be of some assistance. In order to become proficient in palaeography, instruction in the initial stages is beneficial, since progress can be monitored, errors rectified and mis-understandings cleared up. The Workers' Educational Association and Extra-Mural Departments of universities often run evening classes or residential courses in the subject, whilst research groups of local history societies offer another means of guided practice.

Another problem which local historians should be aware of, when dealing with medieval records in particular, is that of dating. In the Middle Ages many documents and events were dated according to saints' days or regnal years. Although the former practice had virtually died out by the time of the Reformation, the latter system survived for much longer – so knowing the dates of the kings and queens of England has a use after all! Until 1752, moreover, New Year's Day fell on 25 March (Lady Day) rather than on 1 January and unless one is careful, one might find oneself in the wrong year. To avoid confusion it is a good idea when transcribing information involving dates between 1 January and 24 March to give both the old and the new years. Thus, 16 February 1672 by contemporary reckoning (16 February 1673 by ours) will be written as 16 February 1672/3. For reference purposes readers should obtain a copy of C. R. Cheney's *Handbook of Dates for Students of English History* (Royal History Society, London, 1970).

For many people the advice given above will be unnecessary, as they will already have acquired a basic knowledge of the subject, together with an understanding of some of the techniques used and the sources which can be examined. If not, then an introductory account such as W. G. Hoskins's *Local History in England* (Longmans, London, 1959) should be read. More recently, Philip Riden's book, *Local History: A Handbook for Beginners* (Batsford, London, 1983) provides an excellent guide to the various classes of record, noting where the documents can be found and offering advice on how to analyse them. For further information, readers should leaf though the back numbers of *The Local Historian* (formerly *The Amateur Historian*) for articles dealing with the sources which can be used to research various aspects of the subject. They should also look at local studies already published for guidance on sources and methodology, even in those dealing with communities elsewhere in the country. In this book I have drawn heavily on both sorts of work for technical information and illustrative material. References to them in the text should be followed up through the footnotes for each chapter at the end of the book.

In general, I have assumed that readers have already been introduced to the study of local history and do not need the basic concepts spelled out. This book therefore builds upon the information presented in the general works such as the ones mentioned above and complements rather than replaces them. The account is not intended to be an exhaustive one, however, for apart from the profusion of sources some are more informative than others. A selection has to be made, and this has been based upon the consideration of what constitutes a practical programme for the historian of local agriculture. As a result, whilst the major classes of documentation for the Middle Ages are fully dealt with, greater emphasis has undoubtedly been placed on evidence from the sixteenth century onwards. In part, this reflects the less tractable nature of the medieval sources but it is also an indication of the greater volume of material available for the later period.

Part One

FARMING AND THE MARKETING OF AGRICULTURAL PRODUCTS

Although natural conditions predisposed certain areas towards one type of farming rather than another, specialization developed only slowly. For centuries communities supported themselves largely from their own resources or from those of the neighbourhood, growing their own corn and breeding and rearing their own animals. Even when changes were made, many small farmers continued in the traditional manner, 'hedging their bets' by keeping a couple of animals and growing an acre or two of corn. The development of a wider market in agricultural products stimulated the trend towards specialization, primarily affecting the larger farmers because they were the ones with the greatest surpluses to sell. As a result, marketing institutions changed and became more efficient.

The balance between mixed farming and livestock husbandry was not a static one, however. In times of population pressure cereal production increased, whilst in periods of demographic decline or stagnation greater emphasis was given to the keeping of animals. Farmers took other measures to protect their incomes in hard times and to increase their returns in good years. Improvements were made and, as a result, yields increased, animals became bigger and more varied, and techniques were streamlined. Farmers from the late sixteenth century onwards, moreover, were helped by a growing volume of work on agriculture which was published and by the emergence of a more careful and scientific attitude towards the land. Even if large landowners and gentlemen-farmers were the first to be influenced by the literature, the effect gradually percolated down through the various strata of rural society. The foundation of agricultural societies in the nineteenth century also promoted agricultural progress, as did the establishment of research and teaching centres.

Decisions about farming practices were arrived at in various ways. For the medieval period, the manor court was the overriding influence. Even freeholders had to attend and be bound by its decisions. In Tudor and Stuart times the vitality of manorial administration seems to have declined, as enclosure reduced the area of communal farming and as local administrative bodies such as the vestry took over some of its work. In many places the court survived merely to record the transference of copyhold property. Where co-operative farming continued, they remained more viable, fulfilling a need and providing a real service for the local community. To this day the open field farmers of Laxton (Notts.) hold courts where they discuss matters of common interest and plan the organization of the agricultural year.

For a long time the manorial organization provided the means whereby landed estates were administered. In this sphere, too, it was being supplanted in the early modern period by administrative machinery specifically based on the estate. Simultaneously, other changes occured that improved the efficiency of estate management. A more professional approach was adopted, especially on the larger estates where employment was given to an emergent class of specialists such as cartographers, surveyors and land stewards. Better book-keeping had a beneficial effect too; the introduction of the double-entry ledger, for instance, tightened up accounting procedure and made it easier to maintain a check on income and expenditure.

Chapter One

FARMING IN THE MIDDLE AGES

Farming, like many other topics, is often treated in an uneven way in local studies. All too often the narrative begins with the Domesday entry and then skims rapidly over several hundred years of history with scarcely a pause. In the past the pace hardly slowed down before the eighteenth or nineteenth centuries, though recently this headlong rush into modern times has been checked by a general appreciation of probate inventories as a major source of material for the early modern period. In fact, there exists a number of records that can help us understand medieval agricultural practices and which are by no means too difficult for local historians to use. From them, we can examine the ways in which medieval farmers responded to key issues of the time. How, for instance, did they cope with the rising demand for farm produce in the period before the early fourteenth century when population was expanding so rapidly? Conversely, what were the adjustments that were made as a result of the demographic crisis of that century? Can one discern regional variations in farming practice? What improvements were made? More is known of demesne than peasant farming, especially in the late twelfth and thirteenth centuries, a time comparatively rich in documentation. Nonetheless, these records provide evidence of an important aspect of farm production for landlords directly exploiting their demesnes played a vital role in supplying the extra food and other raw materials needed to meet growing demand. With the retreat from direct farming as the fourteenth century progressed, the records become less informative, but the material does not disappear altogether and in some places becomes fuller.

Demesne farming

Although material on peasant holdings is included in the survey, any systematic study of land use on the demesne has to start with the Domesday Book. Only the demesne arable is specifically listed, though, of course, the lord would have had his share in the other resources mentioned – pasture, meadow, woodlands, wastes and so on. Arable land, in general, was given the fullest treatment; it was certainly recorded with far greater consistency than other forms of land use and was more likely to have been accurately appraised. The number of plough teams on the demesne indicates the arable acreage there but should be taken only as a rough estimate (see discussion of medieval measurements, below).

The main survey, the Exchequer Domesday, has little to say about individual crops, apart from meadow land, nor does it note the types of animals kept – with the obvious exception of draught oxen and, to a lesser extent, pigs. The Exeter and Little Domesday surveys (the first an earlier and fuller draft of the final document) contain more detailed information on the demesne livestock, and local historians in the South-west and in East Anglia respectively are therefore much better served than their counterparts elsewhere in the country. Little Domesday even records stock numbers at dates earlier than 1086, but only in Essex do the figures offer meaningful contrasts. Sheep, in general, seem to have been more important than cattle, but in places the reverse was true, and in some districts we can see the emergence of dairy farming.[1]

At this point some comment on the measurements used in the Domesday Book and other medieval surveys is called for because, as they were imprecise and variable, they can cause errors in calculation if employed in an uncritical way. When we look at the Domesday survey one of the first problems that confronts us is to assess the size of the ploughland. Conventionally, it has been reckoned as 120 acres, the notional amount of land that could be ploughed by the standard ox-team in a year. Leaving aside the fact that many peasant teams, at least, comprised fewer than eight oxen, the speed of ploughing depended upon the terrain and the nature of the soil.

Ploughlands, moreover, have often been equated with carucates and hides, units of assessment in northern and eastern England and in the rest of the country respectively. As a result, these measurements, together with their sub-divisions, the ox-gang (one-eighth of a carucate) and the virgate (one-quarter of a hide) have often been given a specific acreage which is not always borne out by the evidence. The term 'carucate' does derive from the Latin word for plough or plough-team but, even if it had once referred to the area ploughed by a team, by 1086 it had become a fiscal measure (as had the hide). Similar difficulties are encountered when dealing with oxgangs and virgates, the measurements most commonly used in medieval surveys to denote the size of standard peasant holdings. On individual manors all occupiers of equivalent holdings tended to owe the same rents and services (see below, p. 137). It does not follow, however, that they all farmed exactly the same amount of land. Where the size of the oxgang and the virgate are known, they often do approximate to 15 and 30 acres respectively, but this is not always the case – even on the same estate. On the lands of Gloucester Abbey, for instance, the virgate varied from 28 to 64 acres.

Acres were not precise measurements either. Customary acres, referred to in documents as field acres or acres as they lie, were of indeterminate size, though some sort of rule of thumb guide was common. They might be one, two or more strips in extent, whilst small strips might be called half- or quarter-acres. The Cornish acre contained 40 to 60 statute acres! Measured (or statute) acres were used as well, especially from the thirteenth-century, when actual measurements of the land began to be regularly taken. Each statute acre should equal 160 perches, therefore making it easier to estimate the size of parcels of ground. However, as the length of the perch varied, some statute acres were larger than others. Unfortunately, surveys rarely indicate the type of acre employed and one can only assume that land is being measured in statute acres if dimensions smaller than a quarter-acre are recorded. On the other hand, uniformity in the acreage of different holdings implies the adoption of fiscal acres.[2]

In 1279 an even more ambitious survey was undertaken by Edward I. Known as the Hundred Rolls because the material was supplied by juries meeting at hundred or wapentake courts, the enquiry was never completed, and information exists for only eight counties. Huntingdonshire, Oxfordshire and south Cambridgeshire are well covered, whilst six hundreds of Suffolk and four of Buckinghamshire have extant material. In Bedfordshire, Leicestershire and Warwickshire details from two hundreds are available. Similar information was recorded as in the Domesday survey, and a comparison between the two can be made. The arable acreage is once more emphasized, though occasionally estimates of meadow, enclosed pasture and woodland on the demesne are also recorded.[3]

Estate surveys, extents and terriers provide another contemporary source of information. Surveys describe the land on the demesne, normally based upon the sworn testimony of a local jury rather than upon actual measurement, though this may have been undertaken. Extents contain similar information but also give a valuation for each piece of land. Terriers too may merely describe the demesne but a number denote all the lands of the manor. Inquisitions *post mortem* (IPMs), recording the rights and properties of tenants-in-chief after their death, also contain extents. Only lay estates were dealt with because church land was in corporate ownership.[4] In contrast ecclesiastical properties are better represented in manorial extents and surveys than lay ones. The most informative and detailed extents are those made for large estates, and, of course, villages located on them tend to be better documented than others. Nonetheless, many tenants-in-chief were modest landowners and their IPMs help to fill in gaps in the record.

In all these surveys the farmland of the demesne is set out in detail, and evidence is also given of other forms of land use such as wastes, woods, parks and ponds. In spite of the problems of under-recording (IPMs are somewhat suspect) and a certain lack of precision in measuring pastoral land, they can be used to establish the general pattern of land use on an estate, revealing differences of emphasis between individual manors and showing changes over time. The importance of arable cultivation on the demesne in the period up to the early fourteenth century can plainly be seen, in many areas pointing out startling contrasts with later farming practice. Clearly, demesne farming provided a good deal of the corn needed to feed the growing population. Differences between estates can be discerned, however. Extents of demesne land in Devon in the late thirteenth and early fourteenth centuries indicate variations in land use between the southern and eastern parts of the county. In the south more enclosed pasture could be found, with a correspondingly lower proportion of open waste than in the east. The east, with its numerous, well-watered valleys, also possessed more meadowland. Another development which can be picked up in the documentation is the shrinking acreage of arable land in the early fourteenth century as population pressure lessened even before the Black Death.[5] As Professor Beresford has observed, 'Even a casual study of the extents among the inquisitions *post mortem* show

many examples of land lying uncultivated'.[6] Supporting
evidence for this trend can be obtained from the *Nonarum
Inquisitiones* of 1342, a tax on one-ninth of the value of corn,
wool and lambs produced in the harvest year ending 1341. In
many instances the local juries explained that the fall in the
value of their contribution was due in part to the amount of
land that had gone out of cultivation.[7]

The valuations given in extents and IPMs suggest differences in the relative fertility of land on different manors.
This could relate to the cultivation of land less suited to crops
but undertaken to increase the acreage of corn required to meet
a rising demand. On the Bishop of Worcester's estate at the
end of the thirteenth century the superiority of lowland arable
is revealed in the higher valuations per acre for land lying in the
river valleys and in central Worcestershire than in manors in
the northern part of the county and in the Cotswolds. The
value of pasture also varied enormously.[8] Closes and furlongs
in the open fields were often assessed at different rates,
indicating the relative quality of the land and perhaps reflected
in the names ascribed to them.

The prime source of farming practices in the Middle Ages,
however, is the manorial account, the central document of
estate administration.[9] The day-to-day running of a manor
was the responsibility of the reeve, sometimes assisted by
other men such as the beadle and the hayward. These officials,
normally unfree tenants, were compelled to serve, though at
times they were chosen by their fellow villeins. The reeve, in
turn, was answerable to the bailiff, who had the care of two or
three manors, whilst the oversight of the whole estate was
given to the steward. The latter travelled from manor to
manor, checking on the work being done by the bailiffs and
reeves and holding the manor courts. Exercising financial
oversight, the lord of a single manor might well audit his
reeve's account himself. On larger estates, however, a receiver
did the job for him. On the biggest estates there were several
receivers, all under the control of the receiver-general. The
accounting method used was the charge/discharge system; in
the charge the accountant listed all the money and goods he
had to answer for, against which he set the discharge,
recording all items of expenditure.

The earliest accounts were made in the early twelfth century
and a few survive for that period, but as the habit of keeping
written records had not yet become universal some large

estates had not adopted the practice. Nonetheless, the idea spread rapidly in the second half of the twelfth century, even among lords of single manors, and the number of extant accounts rises dramatically. In the earliest stage, which lasted until about the mid thirteenth century, accounts were produced by auditors at the centre of the estate, and often all that remains are the enrolled accounts, the abstracts of the accounts of individual manors. In the following one hundred years or so, a time when demesne farming flourished, the system of accounting changed. Now the accounts were drawn up on the spot by local officials who then presented them at the audit. From the mid fourteenth century, however, landowners withdrew from demesne farming because of the problems caused by the dramatic fall in the population. As a growing number of demesnes were leased out, details of the agricultural organization disappear.

All historians can benefit from the wealth of information contained in the locally produced accounts in particular, but for non-specialists the uniformity in the organization of the material makes it easy for them to locate individual items, even in long and complex documents. On the front of the roll is written the cash account, divided into the charge and the discharge. On the back (dorse) of the document an account of the various items – corn, livestock, produce and so on – is set out in the same fashion with a charge and discharge section entered for each commodity. The accounting procedure for animals is a little cumbersome since the accountant had to take into consideration the fact that young stock grew up and therefore moved from one category to another. This can lead to mistakes if the researcher is unaware of what the accountant is doing. Other pitfalls await the unwary. The accounts cannot always be taken at face value since some of the entries were made for book-keeping purposes, that is, they represent fictitious sales, adjustments designed to straighten up the account whenever an item was disallowed by the auditor. Similarly, as from the fourteenth century there was a tendency for lords to set fixed targets for livestock and crop yields, 'paper' sales had to be included to balance the books whenever a shortfall occurred. On the other hand, a bumper harvest might not be recorded in the accounts at all. It should be remembered too, that cash entries often indicate the sums allowed by the auditor and that they were not necessarily the amounts spent. Moreover, it must be remembered that the accounts do not necessarily provide an accurate picture of production on the demesne but detail merely what contractual responsibilities were agreed by the lord with his estate official. This problem grew more severe over time as the accounting procedure became more rigid.

In the earliest phase, in the enrolled account, the emphasis on arable farming is reflected in the greater prominence given to that form of husbandry. Information on livestock may be omitted altogether or entered merely as a list of stock. As time passed, the accounts became more comprehensive and detailed in content and more uniform in format, a trend which continued in the locally produced accounts of the subsequent period. Evidence of the type of husbandry being practised can be obtained, as well as specific information on corn, livestock and produce. The documents are often extremely long and very detailed, distinguishing, for instance, between different qualities of grain and and animals of various ages.

Apart from describing the crops grown, the accounts indicate the yields that were achieved. To obtain the information two consecutive accounts are needed because the product of the crop was only entered when thrashed (listed in quarters and bushels) and therefore appears in the year following the one in which it was harvested. From this, one can look at trends in productivity. For comparisons between manors one needs to know the particular measures employed for there were different ones used in the country. The various ways in which fertility was maintained can also be found. There are numerous references to the costs of carting and spreading animal manure and other fertilisers. Signs of progress appear too. In east Norfolk, one of the most densely populated parts of the country in the late thirteenth and fourteenth centuries, rotations were intensified and in places fallows eliminated. This was achieved through large applications of manure and expanding the cultivation of legumes which fixed nitrogen in the soil and provided additional animal feed.[10] Improved rotations seem to have been fitted into existing field systems rather than the number of fields being altered. Accounts and surveys show that very few two-field communities converted their fields to three in this period.[11]

The section on animals may also be minutely sub-divided, going beyond a basic classification of old and young stock. Consequently, it is possible to analyse breeding and rearing practices. Apart from the usual farm animals, other creatures were included – rabbits, doves, pigeons and fish, for instance. Rabbits were of particular importance in the Middle Ages and early modern period, especially on infertile sandy soils, and were kept for their fur and meat. Fishing and fowling, moreover, formed an integral part of the economy of marsh and fenland communities, and throughout the country fish-ponds provided a source of additional protein for peasant and manorial households alike.

Animal disease, primarily referred to as the murrain, is frequently mentioned. In the main, the information appears in the discharge section of each type of animal affected, though if their hides and fells had been sold it is recorded in the cash charge account. By counting up the number of dead animals it is possible to determine the impact that disease had upon the farming economy of the demesne and to pinpoint years of high morbidity. The figures suggest that mortality rates were commonly quite high and that until the second and third quarters of the fourteenth century sheep suffered to a far greater extent than cattle. At Sevenhampton, a Wiltshire manor of the Bishop of Winchester, on average only 117 lambs survived from the flock of 181 ewes that was kept there in the years 1269–81. In bad years, as at the time of the 'common' mortality of the mid 1280s or in the years 1315–22, the rate went even higher.[12]

Peasant farming

A considerable amount of land lay outside the demesne. Indeed, peasant holdings usually occupied a far greater acreage of land on the manor than did the demesne and this proportion grew in the late Middle Ages. Much less is known about the activities of such farmers, however. There is no single source like the manorial account to give a detailed picture, so the local historian is reduced to gleaning whatever information he can from a range of sources. Individually each class may yield only a few crumbs of evidence, but taken together they can help to build up a reasonably convincing picture of events.

The Domesday Book and the Hundred Rolls of 1279 both give general estimates of peasant, as well as demesne, plough-lands. From these figures it is possible to calculate the proportion of arable land tilled by the peasantry and therefore its relative importance to them. The Hundred Rolls generally list demesne land in carucates whilst peasant land, noted in individual holdings, is recorded in virgates. These surveys provide indirect information too. The peasantry had access to local resources such as woodland, moor and marsh and grazed their animals there. Similar evidence can be obtained from manorial extents and surveys; they give some indication of peasant arable, though everything else has to be inferred. Terriers, on the other hand, may deal with all the land of a township and are therefore of greater value. Others refer to the property of an individual, especially a freeholder, for they often accompany a conveyance of land from one person to another.[13] Surveys, extents, custumals (lists of tentants, their holdings and the services they owed their lord) and rentals show that peasant farmers were keeping animals and grazing them on the commons. Various entries in the surveys of Kempsey (Worcs.) in 1288 and 1299, for example, reveal that individuals rendered pigs and geese to the lord, paid him pannage for letting them run their pigs in the wood or gave him money for grazing rights.[14]

Manorial accounts provide some information, though it is uncertain in its incidence. The most regular occurrences are the lists of animals acquired by the lord as either heriots or strays. The heriot was a death duty paid whenever a tenant died and comprised his best beast or good. Particularly good evidence is available on those occasions when the lord had to administer the holding of a peasant, because of the lack of a suitable heir, because the person had run away or because he was a convicted criminal. In such circumstances, the accounts should record the overall situation on the farm. When William Shail of Hatton in Hampton (Warwicks.) fled the manor in June 1377 he left his crops behind to be harvested by his lord;[15] 35 acres had been sown, with a slightly greater acreage being allocated to spring sown crops – barley (12 a.), peas (7 a.) and oats (1 a.) occupied 57 per cent of the land and wheat (8 a.) and rye (7 a.) 43 per cent.

Manor court rolls are another important source of information, revealing the day-to-day organization of the peasant community. Unfortunately, medieval examples are very difficult to read. They were written in Latin and in a crabbed hand with much abbreviation and are virtually indecipherable to the non-expert. However, a number of collections have been published by local record societies. Essentially, the court was an administrative rather than a judicial body which oversaw the social and economic life of the community, though it did fine people who did not abide by its regulations. The steward, as the lord's representative, presided over the court. To help him he had a jury of local inhabitants who presented matters to be dealt with at the court, giving reports or making accusations in response to specific questions asked by the steward (see Appendix 1.) Much of the work was carried out at the court baron, the main administration arm of the manor. There, manorial officials were chosen, farming practices regulated, land conveyed and the peasantry supervised. Among the topics that the court dealt with were the rotations to be adopted in the open fields, the crops to be grown there and arrangements for animals to graze in the fallow field or on the aftermath.

In many manors, where lords had been given special judicial rights from the Crown, court leets were also held, with the authority to determine minor transgressions against the law. Most commonly, the privilege granted was the ancient right of view of frankpledge, whereby tithing groups within the manor presented fellow-inhabitants for various misdemeanours. Cases concerning theft or actions of debt and trespass may provide valuable snippets of information. Animals regularly broke free and trampled down growing corn, offences for which their owners were presented at the court. Often the general term 'corn' (bladum) was given, but specific crops were sometimes noted. At a court held at Pachesham (Surrey) in July 1322, for instance, various animals did damage to vetches, mixed corn and oats growing in the fields.[16] Over time, the number of entries would accumulate, providing evidence of the sort of crops being grown and the popularity of each. Apart from ordinary arable crops, industrial crops like hemp and flax might be named.[17] They appear for instance, whenever people were presented for retting the crops in streams or whenever they ploughed up parcels of the waste to sow them. Information on other aspects of arable cultivation can also be found. At Romsley (Worcs.) marl was spread on the land in 1281. The same roll suggests that a three-course rotation was being employed in the fields: Henry de Fulfen acquired a selion of land for 11 crops, seemingly for 16 years, implying a system of two crops and a fallow.[18]

Livestock are also mentioned in the rolls, though in the same unsystematic way. Regulations were made for the management of livestock, especially their grazing on the fallows and commons. Evidence of fold courses and other practices turn up. Stinting agreements, limiting the number and type of animals that can be kept on a common, also appear. Animals are recorded in other entries as subjects of actions of theft or debt. Others trespassed on the growing corn and were put in the village pound. There, they were joined by other strays which, like heriots, should appear in the manorial accounts. As with crops, inferences can be drawn from the number and type of animals mentioned in the rolls.

Deeds provide incidental evidence too. Pre-Conquest charters contain minor place names and descriptions of land through which the boundaries passed. At Himbledon (Worcs.) in c. 977 the edge of the estate at one point ran 'along the hedge to the rye growing croft, along the headland of the croft to the other headland, from that headland to the barley growing croft'.[19] This means merely that the ground in a particular croft was suitable for a certain grain rather than it being used exclusively for it. In the two centuries after the Conquest the number of deeds multiplied as the practice of keeping records became more commonplace and spread more widely through the community. No longer do they merely refer to the transmission of whole estates but also record sales (and leases) of small portions of land. As a result, more details are given and these can yield information on crops and stock, rotations and other forms of land management.

Final concords also provide evidence of general land use on individual farms, including many belonging to people below the level of gentry. They were drawn up to accompany a fictitious lawsuit, in which the parties to a sale colluded in an action concerning the ownership of the property in order to obtain a legal record of the transaction. Each party was given one copy of the tripartite indenture, and the third part, the 'foot' of the fine, was enrolled in the Court of Common Pleas at Westminster. These records, which originated in the twelfth century and were only discontinued in 1834, have been deposited in the PRO in Chancery Lane.

Such fines are particularly valuable for the study of local agriculture in upland and pastoral areas where communal farming was relatively unimportant and manorial control lax. Records of manorial administration there tend to be few and uninformative. Much of the land was held by small peasant freeholders largely exempt from manorial obligations, who from an early date regularly transferred land by deed or some other device. Fines do give acreages for different types of land involved in the sale but much doubt has been cast on their accuracy. According to A. A. Dibben, the acreages were merely 'approximations'.[20] F. G. Emmison, on the other hand, takes a different point of view. Basing his opinion on a comparison of early-modern fines in the Essex Record Office with their related deeds, he concludes that most fines were 'reasonably correct both as regard areas and qualities of land'. Some rounding up did occur but this was not excessive. Local historians, therefore, can, with care, use them to look at individual farms within their community or employ them *en masse* to find distinct agricultural regions.

Medieval tax records may also be used and, because they have a limited vocabulary, can be examined with profit by the non-specialist. Lay subsidies before 1334 record individual taxpayers and, where local assessment rolls survive, give details of corn and livestock. Of course, the evidence has to be treated with extreme caution, especially the figures for corn which have clearly been under-recorded.[22] Nonetheless, they probably represent the balance of crops being grown in the areas concerned. Animals, it seems, were assessed much more accurately. When clerical income was taxed in 1291 tithe receipts were among the items included. In part, these figures are directly comparable with the returns of the *Nonarum Inquisitiones* of 1342: the tithe of the first tax (roughly) equals one-ninth of the goods of 1342 after tithe had been taken.

Tithes, dues paid to the church avowedly to maintain the minister, feature among the muniments of ecclesiastic establishments. Tithes on land were of two sorts: predial tithes were paid on the fruits of the earth – corn, hay, wood, fruit and other crops – whilst mixed or agistment tithes were assessed on livestock and animal products – young stock, wool, milk, eggs and honey. Rectors enjoyed both kinds of tithes. In parishes where a vicar had been installed, the impropriator (the tithe owner) took the great tithes (normally, but not always, equated with the predial tithes) and the vicar whatever was left over.[24]

In the Middle Ages tithes were paid largely in kind, and therefore the documentation should indicate the types of animals kept and the crops grown. On the Leicester Abbey estate, early-fourteenth-century returns imply a rotation of barley in one field and wheat, with some rye and beans and peas, in the other. Later in the century the proportion of legumes gathered in tithe increased with a corresponding decline in the amount of wheat and barley taken, revealing a change in the cropping arrangements in the fields.[25] The size of herds and flocks can be calculated too. At Cleeve (Worcs.) at the end of the fourteenth century tithes paid on lambs and wool suggest that between 1,020 and 1,340 new lambs were born each year.[26] Similar information should appear in tithe agreements, drawn up between monastic or episcopal rectors and their vicars to define what tithes were due to each party.

Summary

Undoubtedly, there are certain problems which agrarian historians will encounter when examining farming practices in the Middle Ages. The documentary coverage around the country is patchy; survival rates vary from area to area, whilst everywhere demesne farming is better documented than peasant farming. There are difficulties in interpretation, too, partly because of uncertainty in the measurements used or under-recording of the material but also because it is not always clear what the material signifies. Readers should not be discouraged from attempting a study of medieval agriculture, however. Some of the sources are detailed and informative and are relatively easy to use. National and local records exist, and a range of documents can be looked at to fill in the general picture. In particular, in the manorial account medievalists have an invaluable source. Scholars have long worked on them but their importance needs to be more widely known and the information they contain more fully exploited.

Chapter Two

FARMING IN THE EARLY MODERN PERIOD

Early-modern farmers had to contend with a set of circumstances that in many ways were very similar to the ones their medieval predecessors faced. A rapid population growth in the late sixteenth and early seventeenth centuries which increased demand for farm produce was followed by a period of stagnation in which prices fell. Disease was also a factor in reducing the level of population but it played a less dominant role. Not only did fewer people die but, as the countryside was largely unaffected, the towns could be repopulated much more easily. In some respects the response of farmers remained the same. To increase output in the first phase additional land was brought into cultivation and rotations were intensified. New crops and techniques were also introduced.

This positive approach persisted into the period of depression. Landlords did not retreat from demesne farming to the same extent, and improvements continued to be made. These were undertaken in order to maintain income in a difficult time. Only through greater efficiency, that is, by reducing unit costs, could farming be made to yield a profit. Thus, although much arable land was laid down to grass, especially on heavy clay land, compensatory increases took place on the lighter soils. Rotations were further improved by the more extensive use of grass leys or by the insertion of root crops and rotational grasses into the system. The late seventeenth and early eighteenth centuries, in fact, marked a critical phase in the 'agricultural revolution', a time when many of the key features were developed.

Landowners also used legislative means in an attempt to keep up the price of agricultural products during this period of depression. In particular, laws concerning grain dealing were relaxed, and in 1670 the export of grain was allowed whatever the price. In 1672, at a time when complaints about falling rents were rife, corn bounties were introduced on exports. Duties on exported grain were removed in 1689, a measure which was complemented by raising barriers against imports. Action was also taken against imports of Irish cattle and dairy produce.[1]

The estate

Because of the greater range of documentation in the early modern period, more is known about the activities of ordinary farmers. Less reliance therefore needs to be placed on material which deals with the demesne. Nonetheless, many large land-owners continued to maintain a home farm, even when economic conditions turned against agriculture in the post-Restoration period. A proportion of the produce was destined for consumption within the household but much of it was sold off the estate and distributed to a wider market. Demesne farming had an impact on agriculture in another way; many improved practices read in books or borrowed from abroad were first of all tried on the demesne and, if successful, were emulated by other farmers in the locality. On a number of estates, moreover, landowners positively influenced their tenants by inserting improving clauses into their leases. The adoption of a more professional attitude towards administration on a number of estates also had an effect, and improvement and efficiency became the desired goals on many, if not all, estates. Because of such developments, estate records should tell local historians a good deal about agricultural progress in their area, though they must also look at other documents to see what was happening on other farms.

There was a certain amount of continuity between the estate records of the Middle Ages and those of the early modern period. Manorial accounts continued to be made for some time, and the old charge/discharge system of accounting began to give away to double entry book-keeping only after the Restoration. Changes in format were made, however. Many estate accounts did not list items by subject but were arranged chronologically under the headings of receipts and disbursements. This makes the task of finding specific information somewhat time-consuming. Sometimes, separate receipt and disbursement books were made, at others a single ledger was used. For the latter, sections on income and expenditure were often placed opposite each other on a double page. Unfortunately, because items of expenditure were far more numerous than entries concerning income, the two columns quickly moved out of synchronization.[2] Moreover, in many cases insufficient consideration was given to capital tied up in the form of stock. Inventories of stock were kept separately from the main accounts, and there was a tendency for special books, dealing with specific commodities, to appear. Examples include the Dogthorpe cattle book of the Fitzwilliam family of Northamptonshire, the horse book of Sir Richard Newdigate of Arbury Hall (Warwicks.)[3] and the sheep accounts of the Willoughbys of Wollaton (see Appendix 3).

The mode of presenting the figures clearly makes it difficult to gain a complete record of income and expenditure. In some lists items have plainly been left out and there are many examples of slapdash accounting procedures. Even contemporaries found it a problem. In the mid seventeenth century Francis Parker when auditing lord Brook's accounts, wrote on the abstract,

> It is extremely difficult if not Impossible to maker a just estimate of What hath binn cleared out of the revenew this yeare because It doth not appeare what part of the profitt of the stock at Knowle was the product of this yeare & what was stock bought in or laid up in former yeares nor doth he particularly prize the beast he bought in nor how long he kept them nor what they respectively came to per weeke whilst they were kept.[4]

In spite of their deficiencies estate accounts remain an invaluable source of information for local historians, enabling them to build up a picture of agricultural practices on the demesne and to spot any changes and developments that occurred. Information on arable cultivation may include details of the preparation of the land – ploughing, harrowing and manuring, for instance – and times of sowing and harvesting. Material on sowing rates and yields can also be obtained, as can details of rotations and evidence for the introduction of new crops and techniques. The records also provide information on the care and management of animals, as well as indicating the types of livestock kept and their functions. Breeding methods can be examined, as well as other livestock enterprises such as rearing and fattening. The part played by animals in a mixed farming economy is revealed in references to practices like sheep folding on the fallow or to the employment of horses or oxen as draught animals. The integration of the resources of an estate is shown in the movement of animals from one part to another.

Apart from the routine of estate management, the ideas and views of the land agent or the landowner may also be set down, perhaps as a gloss in the margin of the accounts or more fully in commonplace books and diaries. Such comments can certainly be found in letters that passed between steward and landowner whenever the latter was away from the estate. The degree of independence exercised by a steward varied, but even if he enjoyed considerable autonomy, he would keep his master informed of his actions. In particular, changes in the management of the estate were discussed, views expressed and decisions taken. As a result, one can gauge prevailing attitudes towards developments that were taking place in agriculture.

The landowners' reaction to changes in the economic climate may be seen in the fluctuating size of the demesne, as recorded in manorial and estate surveys. At Rushock (Worcs.) surveys of the Wolverhampton Grammar School estate show that, as the price of farm goods went up in the late sixteenth and early seventeenth centuries, the demesne increased in size.[5] Another response, of course, was to raise or lower rents rather than changing the acreage of the demesne. Surveys also record changes in the acreage of crops and grass. In early-modern surveys similar information is often given for copy and leasehold land, which makes it possible to assess if any change on the demesne was a general one or not. At Rushock, for instance, surveys of 1572 and 1654 show a shift from mixed farming towards livestock husbandry, a trend that was noticeable on both the demesne and the copyhold farms. Not all land put down to grass became permanent pasture, however, but was subject instead to a system of convertible husbandry. This was a technique designed to improve the fertility of the soil by regularly changing the land use. At Rushock, the demesne close called Sinderlands was under grass in 1572 (13 a.), corn in 1654 (15 a.) and grass in 1669 (14½ a.)[6]

At Rushock no information about land use on freehold properties is given but elsewhere this may be recorded. The survey of the royal manor of Settrington (East Riding), taken in 1599/1600, is particularly detailed; in the introduction to the printed edition published by the *Yorkshire Archaeological Society* in 1962 A. Harris noted that 'Mansfield (the surveyor) spared no pains to obtain a detailed information. The nature of each holding; character of the common fields; the extent of the woods; the house-types and the village mills – none of these things escaped his notice'.[7] On this manor there were considerable differences in land use between the demesne and the other farms. Much of the demesne had already been enclosed, making pastoral land relatively more important there (63.2 per cent) than on the freeholds (35.9 per cent) and the tenants' farms (33.9 per cent on the 'husbandries' and 49.7 per cent on the smaller 'grassfarms'), which had a much greater proportion of open field land. Cottage holdings, on the other hand, were largely under grass too (78.1 per cent).[8]

Care should still be taken when analysing the figures given in documents like surveys. Medieval terms such as 'virgate' and 'yardland' remained in use as areal measurements, whilst customary acres were also employed. In the glebe terrier of Stanton Lacy (Shrops.), drawn up in 1607, the vicar and the parishioners noted before listing the church land that 'by the word Acre we do not mean an acre by the kings Measure but such a quantity of ground as we among our Selves do hold and account for an Acre'.[9] It was also common practice for land to be measured according to the amount of grain needed to sow it – and some grains were sown more thickly than others.[10]

In the early-modern period leases became more numerous and covered a greater range of estates. Often the land was described field by field, with the names, acreages and state of cultivation being given. Moreover, through covenants inserted in leases owners could control the manner in which their tenants farmed the land, at the same time prescribing penalties for non-compliance. At first, landlords contented themselves with exhorting their tenants to 'farm in a husband-like manner' and to 'commit no waste', but gradually the instructions became more precise, defining more closely the practices to be adopted. Covenants, therefore, might stress the need to keep the land in good heart by manuring or by forbidding overtillage, especially in the last years of a lease. In this way, instead of unscrupulous tenants being able to impoverish the land, the property might actually come back in hand in an improved condition, enabling the landowner to raise the rent. As John Bridgeman told his Shropshire agent, John Jones, on 8 December 1739, I 'would have you view the tenement and send me a note what pieces of tillage land is proper to be laid down to artificial grass for the last three years of this term that the ferme may come to hand in good heart to any succeeding tenant upon a new term'.[11]

Many deeds record an agreement made between various parties and, as such, deal with a wide range of agricultural practice. One such agreement made at Sherington (Bucks.) in 1722 refers to the introduction of temporary leys into the common fields there and, incidentally, to the interrelationship between animals and corn in a mixed farming system of husbandry.[12] More grass was required, it was stated, because of insufficient pasture ground in the open fields to maintain a flock of sheep sufficient to fold the land. Moreover, given the need to keep a requisite number of horses and cows on the farms, there was an inadequate supply of meadow land or enclosed pasture ground to feed them. The leys, it was felt, would remedy this defect.

Agreements were commonly drawn up to settle disputes of one kind or another. Appeal was often made to the conciliar courts, and information on the cases heard appear in their records. Where large landowners were involved, copies may also be found among the estate papers. Among the various disputes affecting farmers in Shropshire one can find references to the growing of saffron and hops on enclosed fenland in a case heard in the Court of Requests in 1549; to the quality of the local March wool in a Chancery suit of 1574; to the intermittent cultivation of the wastes in the records of the Council of the Marches of Wales in 1576; and to the operation of the open fields in depositions heard by the commissioners sent from the Exchequer in 1612.[13]

Where various categories of estate record overlap, a more rounded picture emerges, whilst runs of documentation help to show developments over time. This point can be illustrated by reference to the activities of Sir Edward Filmer of East Sutton Place (Kent).[14] Sir Edward took an active interest in the running of his estate and between 1722, when he inherited the property, and his death in 1755 he devoted much time to it. The records illustrate all aspects of estate management but are particularly good on the running of the home farm. As a starting point, a map of 1703 can be used to show the location of the farm in relation to the mansion house and to reveal the names and acreages of all the fields on the demesne. This map, when examined in conjunction with a particular of $c.$ 1722, provides an overall framework for an analysis of Sir Edward's farming activities based upon the detailed notes and accounts he made. The crops growing in each field were recorded, which shows that he had adopted a variation of the Norfolk system modified to suit local conditions. Elsewhere in the accounts, information was given on sowing rates and the product of each field, enabling yields to be calculated. As he also noted his inputs – the cost of preparing and fertilizing the ground, and payments to labourers – an appraisal of the profitability of his enterprise can be made. Interestingly, Sir Edward, was involved in growing hops and fruit, traditional aspects of Kentish farming.

Other early modern sources for agriculture

For a general account of the pattern of farming in an area, local historians may find the topographical works of the time useful. These accounts vary in quality and detail but do provide a valuable perspective on contemporary practice and one which can be brought into sharper focus by further research among the documents. Many of the observations are not specific, the writer merely giving a general impression of the countryside through which he or she passed, but, even so, they give an overall description of land use. Thus, when commenting on Warwickshire, John Leland, who toured England in the 1540s, remarked upon the division of the county between the Arden half ('plentifull . . . of grasse and woode') and the felden half ('plentifull of corne').[15] Greater detail is provided for other areas. Of the area between the River Trent and Melton Mowbray (Leics.) Leland observed 'many benes and peson, as yt is communely thorough Leyrcestreshir'.[16] Pastoral farming was not neglected either. In the 1690s Celia Fiennes wrote of Cheshire, 'what I wonder'd at was that though this shire is remarkable for a greate deale of greate Cheeses and Dairys I did not see more than 20 or 30 cowes in a troope feedinge, but on equiry find the custome of the country to joyn their milking together of a whole village and so make their great Cheeses and so it goes round'.[17]

Travellers' accounts can be tested against a source of information that gives more detail on local farming, namely the probate inventory. Inventories were drawn up in conjunction with wills for probate purposes, mainly for the period between the mid sixteenth and eighteenth centuries. In them will be included information on livestock, crops and farm produce and, where fields are named, some evidence of enclosure and farming organization. Because they continued to be made over a considerable length of time, changes and developments in local farming practices can be discerned. Firstly, they indicate the growing diversity of agriculture, with farmers, especially the larger, more market oriented ones, increasingly specializing in the production of certain commodities. Thus, on the north Shropshire Plain, the development of dairy farming is illustrated not only in the prominence given to cows and heifers in the inventories but also in the stocks of cheese and dairy-making equipment listed there.[18] Analysed *en masse* these records help to define farming regions, the boundaries of which transcend those of administrative units such as counties.

Other innovations – the change from ox- to horse draught, improvements in equipment, the introduction of new crops like turnips and clover or the development of more intensive rotations, for instance – can be discovered, though allowance has to be made for the gap between first use and the making of the inventory. For rotations, inventories of open-field farmers are particularly good. It was not uncommon for appraisers to link together in one entry crops growing in each field, and, even if assessed separately, acreages or valuations (duly weighted) provide a clue. At Wigston Magna (Leics.) wheat, rye and barley were normally sown in one of the three fields, and peas and beans in the second. The third lay fallow. Where land lay partly in open fields and partly in closes, field names, if given, suggest the way in which the two were integrated.[19]

Some indication of yields can also be made. This can be assessed by employing a method pioneered by Mark Overton and discussed in an article entitled 'Estimating Crop Yields from Probate Inventories: an Example from East Anglia 1585–1730', published in the *Journal of Economic History*, 39 (1979). The basic premise assumes that a close relationship existed between the estimated value per acre of a growing crop shortly before it was harvested and the valuation per bushel of the same type of corn when in store. Using selected inventories the latter can be divided into the former to give a yield in bushels per acre. Applying a modified version of this method on Hertfordshire inventories for the period 1550–1700 Paul Glennie was able to pinpoint the post-Restoration period as a time when corn yields dramatically improved in the county.[20]

When using inventories local historians must be aware of

certain problems, some of a practical nature and others of a more institutional kind. Firstly, inventories for a parish may be located in a number of different repositories.[21] Probate of wills normally came within the jurisdiction of the diocesan courts and were proved at either the archdeacon's court (generally for people who held property in one place) or the bishop's consistory court (for those with larger estates, if located in a single diocese). However, contentious wills and those of persons holding land in more than one diocese, were dealt with at the two prerogative courts of the archbishops of York and Canterbury. The former are housed at the Borthwick Institute of York and the latter in the PRO in Chancery Lane, London. Naturally, some very important and wealthy individuals had their will proved at the prerogative courts, but there are many wills and inventories of ordinary people there too. There were also some exempt jurisdictions, known as peculiars, outside the control of the church. The location of probate materials derived from such bodies will depend upon the type of peculiar jurisdiction concerned. Seigneurial peculiars, for instance, will be found among manorial and estate collections.

This discussion on status raises the question of the type of people whose goods were appraised. In terms of social class, inventories record the personal estates of a diverse section of the population, ranging from members of the aristocracy at one end, down through the various grades of farmer, to the smallholder at the other. Rural craftsmen and even some labourers are included, but these groups, like the smallholders, are not so well represented because many of them had insufficient personal property to warrant an inventory being made. In spite of the popular misconception that personal estates valued at below £5 did not have to be appraised, in practice some sort of selection process evolved. As a result, the inventory-leaving sector of the population was a minority one, though the proportion fluctuated over time. The numbers involved increased both absolutely and in relative terms in the century after 1550, but thereafter the group became more exclusive. These changes affect the general validity of any results obtained by analysing the data: the material in general is skewed towards the larger farmers and will therefore tend to emphasize the development of specialization, but this bias becomes more pronounced towards the end of the period.

Because inventories record the personal estate of a person

after their decease, they hardly give a typical picture of an individual's normal farming enterprise. Many farmers had retired by the time of their death, perhaps handing over the farm to a son, and even if they were still involved they may well have cut down on their activities. Numerous yeomen, for instance, died leaving only a cow or a few head of sheep. On fully operational farms, moreover, only inventories made between April and October should be relied upon to provide the best lists of livestock and crops. Other inventories should, of course, be examined, and the absence of spring corn in the fields may be compensated for by reference to harvested corn in store.

More fundamentally, some items are under-represented in or excluded from inventories. Legally, animals such as rabbits, fish, pigeons and doves, all found in medieval manorial accounts, did not have to be entered, though all the normal farm animals did. However, rabbits often do appear especially in areas where commercial warrens had been established. Ezekial Archer of Mickleham (Surrey), for instance, had a lease of Box Hill warren, and when his goods were appraised in 1693 he possessed 2,500 conies worth £75.[22] Poultry and bees tend to be under-recorded, the former because they were so commonplace that it was often deemed unnecessary to list them.

The recording of crops presents further difficulties. Only products harvested above ground and whose cultivation owed something to the labour of man had to be entered. As a result, corn is always included but fruit is rarely mentioned, and grass is normally recorded only as hay and trees only after felling. Because of these limitations it may prove more difficult to assess the timing and pace of innovations such as the introduction of new rotations and crops. In practice, the distinction was not always made, however. In any case it could be (and was) argued that, as the new grasses were sown, labour had been expanded in their cultivation. With regard to root crops, moreover, the leaves, often used as animal feed, grew above ground and therefore were liable for inclusion.

Other omissions were accidental. At the bottom of the inventory of Richard Rowley of Wyken, Worfield (Shrops.), made on 7 June 1605, is appended the note, 'Item I the Executor doe valew the lent tyllinge more then it is valued one Leasow being omytted by the praysers'.[23] Some goods were removed before the appraisers came in, perhaps stolen but more often because the legatees had taken them. The lack of horses in the inventory of Thomas Rock of Stourbridge (Worcs.), a noted horse dealer, is perhaps explained by the following entry made in his will earlier in the year. 'My will is that my horses and coltes shalbe sold by my . . . wife & the money . . . accrewing . . . shalbe divided between her & my . . . thre yongest children'.[24]

Where inventories have not survived, some indication of the nature of local agriculture can be obtained from the accompanying wills. References to farm stock abound but are often couched in such vague terms as 'my crop of corn' or 'all my cattle'. Individual bequests of animals, when totalled up, might provide useable information. Nonetheless, omissions, often suspected, are at times explicitly stated, as in references like 'one hundred of my best sheep'.[25] The acreage of crops, too, is difficult to estimate from wills. At a general level, a count of the number of entries for individual crops will give a rough guide to their relative importance, though winter corns, because they were in the ground longer, had a greater chance of being mentioned. References to closes and to open field strips provide information on the organization of the fields, whilst indirect evidence of arable cultivation can also be obtained from the bequests of draught animals and of implements of husbandry like ploughs and harrows.

In this period too, greater use can be made of a pre-existing class of ecclesiastical material, namely tithe records. Documents like tithe account books survive in larger numbers, and if there is a good run of material, as at Fressingfield (Suffolk), developments over time can be discerned.[26] Improvements in local practices – enclosure, more intensive rotations and the introduction of new crops – should appear in the books in the form of improved moduses (small customary money payments in lieu of produce), larger quantities of produce or references to new crops such as clover, turnips and potatoes. In practice, of course, it was never that straightforward. Many tithe owners, for a variety of reasons, were afraid to pursue their claims fully and did not demand all that was legitimately due to them. This undoubtedly affects the books as indicators of change.[27]

Action certainly was taken, as can be seen from the numerous tithe cases that were heard in the courts. These disputes were brought before the diocesan courts or taken to Chancery or the Exchequer, and between them they generated a considerable archive of material. Commonly, conflicts broke out when tithe owners attempted to increase moduses or to impose payment on new crops or on lands newly improved. Their action was hardly surprising given the rapid rise in prices in the late sixteenth and early seventeenth centuries, which made a nonsense of established payments and gave the tithe owners a derisory return. For their part farmers resented paying more in tithes, especially as after the Reformation lay ownership of tithes rose, making it clear to many that tithes were not being used for their proper purpose.

Information on tithes can also be found in glebe terriers, introduced by a canon of 1571 and repeated in 1604. The order directed bishops to see that ministers and churchwardens in each parish compiled a schedule of the endowments of the church there. The bulk of the terriers comprise a description of church property, but other possessions, privileges and sources of revenue were also recorded. When tithes are referred to, particular stress is laid on new crops because they would bring in additional income.[28] At Caverswall (Staffs.) a new section on root crops was begun in 1722, the incumbent recording, 'Tythe in kind of Potatoes, Parsnips, Carriots, Turnips and all manner of roots'.[29]

A similar record of the sources of income had been made in the *Valor Ecclesiasticus*, the survey of church property which preceded the introduction of a new clerical tax in 1535. Whilst the land is not described in the same detail given in the glebe terriers, it does indicate land use. At North Cerney (Glos.), for instance, the glebe comprised 96 acres of arable land and 70 acres of pasture.[30]

Of the other ecclesiastical sources, Easter books may provide evidence of the general nature of local farming. At Adderley (Shrops.) books survive for the 1650s, and the prominence given to milch cows in the lists reflects the growing importance of dairy farming in the area.[31] In mixed farming communities more corn may have been given.

Clearly, the church played an important part in the secular as well as the spiritual life of people living in the countryside, but it was not the only body to do so. In the counties, for instance, the bulk of the administrative work was carried out by the Justices of the Peace (JPs). Though their name is indicative of the judicial role they played, over the course of time they acquired wide ranging regulatory and supervisory powers too. Justices, in general, were drawn from the ranks of the county gentry and, as members of the landed elite, could be relied upon to uphold a system of government based upon status and the ownership of land. In their sphere of influence they wielded considerable power. Judicially, their authority was extensive, whilst administratively they were responsible for the execution of a great deal of social and economic legislation.[32] Among the agricultural matters that concerned them were the regulation of the market, the licensing of middlemen–dealers and the fixing of wages and prices. In years of bad harvests they had a vital role to play in ensuring that the markets were well stocked with farm produce. Every year, moreover, the parish constable sent a list of present-ments to the high constable of the hundred, by now an agent of the justices. The list might include offences like encroach-ment onto the wastes and highways or the failure to scour ditches or maintain hedges in good order, manorial matters, but ones which were increasingly being dealt with at the quarter sessions.

The main organ of administration through which the JPs ran the county was the quarter sessions, though, as the pressure of work increased, some devolution of business occurred. These offshoots eventually turned into the Petty Sessions. Quarter sessions' papers were kept by the Clerk of the Peace, who, in his capacity as *custos rotulorum*, was in charge of the public records of the county. At the end of each quarter session all the records were normally bound together in a single file and rolled up in a parchment cover. In some populous counties the sheer volume of paperwork necessita-ted some division of the material from the outset. The documents are varied, comprising *inter alia* licences, present-ments, indictments, recognizances, petitions and orders. One of the best sources for agrarian historians to use are the depositions of suspects and witnesses. As they were written *verbatim*, they are full of incidental detail and provide numerous and often unexpected insights into the social and economic conditions of the time.

Locally, the manor remained an important administrative unit during the early-modern period, though it un-doubtedly lost some ground to the parish vestry. In particular, it retained its vitality in places where communal agriculture survived, and there the manor court continued as the institu-tion where decisions concerning local farming practices were made. By-laws were promulgated, regulations approved and offenders fined. In fact, the number of by-laws seem to have grown in the sixteenth and seventeenth centuries as population growth put pressure upon the land and its resources.

The parish rose to greater prominence in this period because the government imposed additional duties on it (though in large parishes with scattered settlement the township was often the administrative unit). To the constable and the churchwardens were added the surveyor of the highways and the overseers of the poor. Such officers accounted to the parishioners at a meeting of the vestry, normally held at Easter each year. The vestry had medieval antecendents, having been established at least as early as the fourteenth century for the management of ecclesiastical affairs but in the early modern period it became a general administrative body. Sometimes, notably in populous industrializing parishes or in places where the leading inhabitants formed a cabal, executive committees known as select vestries were set up which excluded most of the population.

As we have seen, the rise of the vestry did not necessarily mean the demise of the manor, and in many places the two bodies co-existed side-by-side. However, it is no coincidence that, as the vestry grew in importance, the manor declined as an institution. The right to set parish rates to finance the work of its officials and to hold them to account at the end of their period of office gave the vestry undoubted prestige. Inevitably, it began to involve itself in every aspect of local administration, making by-laws and issuing instructions to the parishioners on all manner of subjects. In many places, therefore, the regulation of farming and the management of the fields and commons had passed to the vestry. Consequently, vestry minutes might contain evidence of local farming practices and should be consulted, especially if contemporary manor court rolls are uninformative.

Parish rates may also provide an indication of the type of farming being carried out in a locality. They were normally based upon the occupancy of land but occasionally they were assessed on the ownership of animals. At Horbling (Lincs.) five rating lists have survived for the period 1636–1742 and record the stock of horses, cattle and sheep of each individual.[33] As the rate caught in its net people who owned one horse or one beast, it was quite comprehensive and, in fact, gives a more accurate picture of animal husbandry in the parish than do the inventories. The median-sized herds and flocks were consistently lower in the rates, reflecting the wider section of society involved. When comparisons can be made between inventories and the rates or between successive rates, fluctuations in the number of animals kept by individuals is apparent.[34] In general, the stock listed in the inventories tends to be larger than those assessed in the rates, implying that they were under-recorded in the latter.

Interestingly, at a national level surviving returns of the Sheep Tax of 1549 offer other evidence, if of a fragmentary nature, of one aspect of animal husbandry.[35] Existing accounts cover five counties – Devon, Huntingdonshire, Nottinghamshire, Oxfordshire and Yorkshire – but only the returns for Huntingdonshire and, to a lesser extent, Nottinghamshire can be used to draw general conclusions. In Huntingdonshire the commissioners seem to have been conscientious, assessing one man on two sheep grazing on the commons at Huntingdon, and this suggests that a reasonable estimate of the scale and scope of sheep farming in the county can be obtained. Under-recording was widespread, however, and often only one name per village appears on the roll. Certainly, the material does provide some valuable information. At that time, for instance, enclosure for sheep grazing had once more become a matter of concern, and some well-known enclosers turn up in the records. Robert Derwell of Little Gidding (Hunts.), later to enclose the fields and destroy the farmhouses of the village, had a flock of 600 sheep on the commons there in 1549.[36] Other individuals will be of interest to local historians of the communities in which they lived and farmed, though the return will probably have underestimated the size of their flocks. Separate categories for sheep grazing in closes and on commons or in enclosed tillage grounds illustrates differences in local practice.[37]

Summary

Sources of information on agriculture in the early modern period are not always better than those of the Middle Ages and in some instances are inferior. They have certain advantages, however, and this makes the period an attractive one for the non-specialist to study. Firstly, more documents have survived, especially after the Restoration, and this means in effect that a larger number of communities can be examined, and perhaps in more detail too. The documents themselves are easier to read for, apart from the greater use of English and more intelligible style of writing, books and ledgers began to replace scrolls of parchment. The period is an interesting one; dramatic changes took place in agriculture which affected the lives of everyone in the community, and for the first time documents can be used to examine closely the impact of such developments on society at large. In particular, the appearance of probate inventories as a source of information makes it possible for agrarian historians to look at the practice of ordinary farmers.

Chapter Three

MODERN FARMING (from *c*. 1750)

The fortunes of farmers and landowners continued to fluctuate according to prevailing conditions, and their responses to them remained essentially the same. During periods of population growth and high prices a good deal of capital was invested in agriculture so that output could be increased. This was particularly noticeable during the period of 'high farming' that characterized the middle of the nineteenth century, but it did occur in the late eighteenth century and during the years of the French Wars too. Traditional ways of improving produc-tion – specialization, enclosure, intensive rotations (especially through the wider application of root crops and the rotational grasses), the integration of animals and corn and the use of fertilizers – were still employed but carried out in a more systematic fashion. To these should be added technical and mechanical innovations which revolutionized the progress of agriculture. While many of the measures were designed to increase the output of cereals, livestock were not neglected and the size a quality of the animals improved too. Indeed, animals became an even more vital element in the production equation. Of course, not everyone farmed 'high' for ignorance and small farmers remained (though the two did not neces-sarily go together).

At times of depression land tended to be laid down to grass, and farmers retrenched. Critical periods occurred immediately after the Napoleonic War and during the last quarter of the nineteenth century. Large landowners still used their control of parliament to pass measures to help the farming interest. In 1815 the Corn Laws were tightened up, an absolute prohibition being placed on the import of corn unless the price had reached a specific level (80s. 0d. a-quarter of wheat, 40s. 0d. for barley and 27s. 0d. for oats). Further acts followed in 1822, 1828 and 1842, each modifying the earlier measure. Although a *cause célèbre*, the Corn Laws did little to maintain the price of corn and when repealed in 1846 disaster did not strike down the landed interest.[1]

For the local historian the study of agriculture in the

community becomes far easier in this period. The rapid growth of population brought about by industrialization made people more aware of the need for an efficient agricultural sector and this made its fortunes the subject of much greater debate.[2] This is reflected in the space given to agriculture in local and national newspapers, in the works of agricultural writers like William Marshall and Arthur Young, and in the growth in the number of agricultural societies and publications. This growing professional interest in the industry can also be seen in the foundation of the Royal Agricultural Society in 1838 and in the establishment of research and teaching centres: the Rothamstead experimental station was set up in 1843, and Cirencester, the first agricultural college, was opened in 1845.[3] Parliament was involved too, as is illustrated in the number of parliamentary commissions that were set up in the nineteenth century to deal with various agricultural problems. There was also a desire to base the discussion on a firmer foundation by collecting statistics which would inform the people concerned of the true situation. Initial attempts were made during the critical years at the turn of the eighteenth century, but systematic records were not begun until 1866. To these figures can be added the information to be derived from old sources such as estate records and new ones such as tithe awards.

The estate

For the management of the land, estate records still provide the best source of information. The major classes of documentation continue throughout the period but now in greater number and in more detail, reflecting the growth of a more professional attitude towards estate management. Moreover, as there is a greater overlap between the various classes of material, local historians can gain a better understanding of the system of farming being practised. Similarly, longer runs of documentation help to show developments over time. Thus, apart from an appraisal of the minutiae of local agriculture, it is easier to put the account into a wider context.

For an overview of land use and farming systems on an estate surveys can still be used, especially to show changes over time. In particular, the type of survey known as a valuation became more common. Valuations had medieval antecedents, but in later examples, often drawn up by a professional surveyor, land was more accurately measured and valued. Normally, only general land use was recorded but additional information, explaining the valuation and ways in which the income could be improved, was often given (see Appendix 4).

For the demesne, account books remain an indispensable source, providing the sort of evidence that we saw earlier in Sir Edward Filmer's accounts. Moreover, with the development of double entry book-keeping it becomes easier to calculate both inputs and outputs and to observe the system in operation. Apart from the diffusion of the rotational grasses and turnips, already established by the middle of the eighteenth century, local historians should look out for references to new crops such as potatoes, swedes, mangolds and sugar beet and to see how and when they were incorporated into the rotation. The accounts are also more likely to mention specific varieties of grain, and experiments were often conducted to see which sort did best. Animals were described in greater detail as well, as landowners paid greater attention to the qualities of particular breeds and sought to improve their quality by more systematic breeding. As before, the accounts should indicate the ways in which crops and stock were integrated, together with any changes in the weighting given to each aspect as economic circumstances altered. High farming of the middle of the nineteenth century, for instance, required greater stocking rates in order to increase the yields of corn. In this period imported and artificial fertilizers were beginning to have an impact too, and references to them should appear in the accounts.

The information can also be found in a more consolidated form in cropping and stock books, which often combine the functions of inventories and accounts. Although introduced in the early modern period, they became widely used only at a later date as more landowners took an interest in improving the quality of their corn and livestock. In the early nineteenth century, for instance, entries in the stock books of Thomas Coke reflect his decision, after a prolonged trial, to breed Southdown sheep rather than Leicesters. (Incidentally, subsequent sales of his Leicester rams appear in the accounts.[4]) From a similar source we learn that at the end of the century Lord Wantage had Hereford and Shorthorn store cattle and Hampshire Down ewes on his Berkshire estate. He also bred highly prized Shire horses. Later cropping and stock books of the estate reveal changes of land use during the course of the early twenieth century, illustrating the point that such sources can be used to indicate the adjustments made by landowners to new sets of circumstances.[5]

Estate records also provided us with information on farming outside the demesne. Leases become more informative as landowners extended the practice, already inaugurated, of inserting into them clauses which positively influenced the ways in which their tenants farmed. Hitherto, instructions had concentrated on general measures designed to maintain the fertility of the soil and to prevent overcropping (see above p. 36). In the second half of the eighteenth century, leases were sealed which gave landowners greater control and direction over farming methods. The crops to be sown and the rotations to be followed were written down, often in considerable detail. In the nineteenth century fewer leases were made for on a number of estates farms were let on annual tenancies, often without a written agreement. Where the arrangements were written down, either in leases or agreements, the information given was frequently very detailed (see Appendix 5).

As before, commonplace books, diaries, reports and correspondence illustrate a wide range of agricultural topics, some dealing with routine farming and administrative matters, others with specific issues of the time. In 1844, for instance, the tenants on the Wolverhampton Grammar School estate at Rushock (Worcs.) sought the support of the trustees in their fight against the repeal of the corn laws, then entering its final phase. In his report of March 1844 Mr Matthews, the agent, wrote that he had been urged by one of the tenants, Joseph Lett, 'a zealous supporter of the Worcestershire Agricultural Protection Society', to persuade the trustees to uphold their cause.[6] Similarly, evidence of concern can be found during periods of depression. In a letter written to George Norman on 20 April 1879, Lord Overstone confided that, 'my great grievance now is Agricultural distress. To my great surprise my Tenantry are all in confusion. My weak tenants are becoming bankrupt; my richest tenants declare they have lost so much in the last few years, that they can go on no longer.'[7]

To these sources should be added those generated by the farmers themselves. Apart from those kept in the various record offices around the country, the Museum of Rural Life at Reading University has a good collection. However, as R. J. Colyer observes in an article on the subject, 'the nineteenth century tenant farmer who maintained a comprehensive set of meaningful farm accounts was the notable exception rather than the rule'.[8] Even where they survive, they are often difficult to analyse because of the primitive method of accounting adopted and the absence of precise information on inputs. Nonetheless, if used carefully, they can provide insight into local farming practices which were probably more typical of the area than those in operation on the demesne.

Some farmers kept diaries too. Even if readers do not find one for their own community, there may be one written by a farmer from a neighbouring parish or, if not, from one farther afield engaged in a similar form of husbandry. That of John Simpson Calvertt, who farmed Fairspear and High Lodge Farms at Leafield (Oxon.) is particularly interesting.[9] He took the tenancy of the farms in 1875 and in his diary, which continues to 1900, he records the problems encountered by farmers during the depression. For more recent times we have the testimony of the farmers themselves.

General sources of farming

Whilst estate records were constantly being made, many of the other sources comprise single documents, giving information for a particular period. As a result, a range of material has to be used to build up a picture of local farming practices over time. Some are more comprehensive than others, of course, either because of the nature of the source or because of shortcomings in the collection of the evidence. This means that comparisons between one period and another are often only partial ones, but at least local historians can expect to find the information to make them. The documents, moreover, enable them to research all the major changes that occurred in agriculture during the course of the last two centuries.

The response of farmers to increased demand during the late eighteenth century and in the period of the Napoleonic Wars can be gauged from new governmental and literary sources, especially if allied to contemporary estate material. At the turn of the eighteenth century the combination of bad harvests, war and civil unrest worried the government. The Home Office files of the period, deposited at the PRO at Kew, are full of reports of shortages and riots in the provinces and are a useful sources of information for the local historian, if something of a lucky dip. The government, concerned over the supply of foodstuffs, therefore instituted a number of enquiries into the state of agriculture. These returns can also be found among the Home Office papers. Their value to local historians, however, depends upon where they live for the records vary in accuracy, coverage and format. The first survey was taken in 1795 after two poor harvests and deals only with crops. The data is particularly inconsistent since the questions asked were vague and imprecise (among other things, the government wanted local information on yields and comparisons between the 1794 and 1795 harvests). For some counties like Gloucestershire and Lancashire the local returns are numerous, but for many others there is only one overall report. The threat of invasion in 1798 led to the collection of the 'Lieutenancy Records' which cover a number of coastal parishes in southern England and give information on livestock and crops. For local historians of that area they are a useful source. The compilation of the 1800 returns, like the 1795 survey, was a reaction to a bad harvest (1799). It, too, was concerned solely with crops, and especially with the potential yield of the 1800 harvest. Because the scope of the enquiry was more restricted and the questions asked more precise, the evidence is of a more uniform quality. In terms of geographic spread and content the information is superior to that of 1795 but it still remains an uneven and patchy source.[10]

The 1800 harvest was as bad as the previous one and thus another enquiry was ordered. This survey, known as the 1801 crop returns, is the one most popular with local historians. It was parish based, and the responsibility for the collection of the information was given to the incumbent. Having by now gained considerable experience in conducting such a survey, the government organized this one much more effectively than before. Special printed forms were made, with spaces for specific crops – wheat, barley, oats, potatoes, peas and beans. Turnips and rape were bracketed together but in many cases one or other (usually rape) has been scored out, indicating the figure for a single crop. Rye was not included on the list – except in dioceses where the forms were reprinted locally – but it tended to be entered on the forms in parishes where it was grown. Other crops like lentils and flax, similarly omitted, were less likely to be added but on occasion were put in. Thus, the curate of Silkstone (West Riding) wrote that 'peas are always sown with lentils for Horses' Eatage'.[12] Information on fallows, pastures and land sown with rotational grasses was not requested. This is unfortunate for vital evidence of the spread of new rotations involving improved grasses is missing, even if material on root crops is available.

At the side of the form room was left for comments, and these prove to be very interesting. In over half of them (2,790 out of 5,050 returns in England and Wales) evidence of crop yields is given.[13] Ancillary information is given too. At Longford (Shrops.), where 13 acres of potatoes were recorded, the incumbent commented that 'potatoes have turn'd out well; nothing can have been more fortunate for the Poor, as it has been the chief (means) of their support; Bread corn & bocher meat being out of reach of their pockets. And nothing will tend more to check the exorbitancy of the Farmer than attention to the cultivation of this nutritious root'.[14]

Among the problems encountered when analysing the returns is the one of omission. Material is missing for many parishes, and some counties are better served than others. In Wales the gaps seem random, but in Cornwall they mostly relate to moorland or urban parishes where arable cultivation was unimportant.[15] Another difficulty is the variety of measures used. Apart from statute acres, customary acres or corn measures were employed. Most intractable of all, however, is the question of reliability. In some instances we know that the returns were accurate because the incumbent said so. At Badsworth (West Riding) the curate reported that 'this is an accurate return'.[16] More often the minister had to admit that the record was incorrect, giving as the reason the reluctance of farmers to provide information which might led to an increase in their tithe assessment. As the curate of Worsborough (West Riding) wrote,

> I have us'd all my Endeavours to make this Return a correct one, but from the Backwardness of the Farmers in giving me Information & from their evasive Answers to my Inquiries I have Reason to think that the Number of Acres is considerably less than it ought to be.[17]

Because of these difficulties, most historians using the returns have limited themselves to analysing the *relative* importance of the various crops in a particular parish or area. It is generally assumed that, whilst the acreage of individual crops may well have been underestimated, their ranking in relation to one another is correct. Thus, they can be used to compare adjacent parishes or to construct agricultural regions, according to their combination of crops. Of course, the information is better for mixed farming districts because of the greater acreage of cultivated land. In pastoral areas the proportion of land under the plough was smaller and the returns less useful as indicators of local farming practice. The incumbent of the chapelry of Bradfield (West Riding) made this point when he wrote that the area was 'more proper for breeding sheep & other cattle than growing corn'.[18]

The date in these returns can be complemented by contemporary literary and journalistic sources which also provide a context in which to interpret the statistics. Readers should therefore look at the work of agricultural writers like William Marshall and Arthur Young and the county reports commissioned by the Board of Agriculture (a private society established in 1793 and not the forerunner of the later Board (Ministry) of Agriculture set up in 1889). Two reports were published for most counties between 1793 and 1815, invariably by different authors. As a rule, the second series of reports was much better than the first; they are more uniform in content and quality and in general more accurate and informative. The authors had more time to compile their surveys and could use annotated copies of the first reports to guide them. The overall standard, however, varied enormously. Some of the correspondents were farmers or land agents and had had practical experience but others were incompetent.[19]

What the reports do provide is information on certain topics excluded from the returns, in particular evidence of livestock husbandry and grassland management. Comparisons of the two reports also highlight the various changes that were taking place in agriculture at this critical time, even if they emphasize the developments being carried out on the larger farms. Moreover, they contain many interesting insights into local agricultural practice. T. Batchelor, writing in the *General view of the Agriculture of the County of Bedford* (1808), noted of the market gardening area of the county, 'good garden ground where sandy soils prevails in Biggleswade, Clophill and Maulden'.[20] For material on a particular community, however, much depends upon the quality of the report and the thoroughness with which it was prepared.

After the end of the Napoleonic Wars farmers had to adjust to peacetime conditions and in particular to lower prices for their goods. The tightening up of the Corn Laws in 1815 did little to ease the situation. Indeed, the depression affected mixed farmers more severely than their counterparts in pastoral regions, and it was worst in areas where crops were being grown on heavy soils. This caused much distress, and on a number of occasions – 1821, 1833, 1836 and 1837 – the government set up select committees to look at the situation. The committees heard evidence from many parts of the country, and the reports include depositions from individual farmers, commenting upon their experience and giving details of their enterprises. Accounts were presented, revealing the crops grown and livestock kept, and the prices that they fetched. Because of its importance, agriculture was a regular subject of parliamentary enquiry, and in the nineteenth century other commissions were set up to deal with such matters as labour, wages, customs, cattle plague and allotments.

In the late 1830s agricultural conditions improved, and the contrast with the preceding period is apparent in the literary evidence. The county surveys printed in the *Journal of the Royal Agricultural Society of England*, for instance, can be compared with the *General Views of Agriculture* for each county. In general, the essays are more thorough and informed and emphasize innovation and the adoption of new and improved techniques. Those written in the mid century report the spread of high farming methods around the country and chart the expansion of arable cultivation. In particular, much progress had been made in the clays as drainage schemes, financed by cheap government loans, spread. At the same time they record improvements in livestock management; in a number of essays the authors report on the growing use of short-horn cattle and this had the effect of raising dairy production in a number of regions.[21] Like all such accounts, the essays do tend to reflect the views of the larger and more progressive farmers and may give only a partial view of the agriculture of a particular county.

Agricultural journals and magazines, in general, were written in the same vein. In ordinary newspapers the advertisements are the best source of information on the crops and stock of an area. Advertisements placed in the *Gloucester Journal*, for instance, represent an important source of information on market gardening in the Vale of Evesham in the early nineteenth century: potatoes, onions and cabbages are the vegetables most commonly mentioned.[22] Local newspapers also give inventories of crops, livestock and equipment to be sold at farm sales and at auctions, the advertisements having been placed there by the auctioneering firm conducting the business. In a farm disposal sale all the goods were printed, and the list has the appearance of a probate inventory.

For the period of high farming the basic source on land use and agricultural practice is the tithe award. As a result of the Tithes Commutation Act of 1836, which converted the duty into a money payment, commissioners were sent around the country to assess the value of all titheable land. Altogether they surveyed some 11,800 parishes in England and Wales. In some places where parishes were large, as in the northern counties, townships were used as the unit of assessment. Those parishes with a large proportion of titheable land were obviously more thoroughly affected by the measure than others, and there were regional variations too. In areas of parliamentary enclosure, for instance, the coverage is poor. The commissioners did their jobs quickly and effectively; most of the awards had been confirmed by the end of 1844, eight years after the Act was passed, and very few areas remained to be surveyed in the 1850s.[23] When the tithe commissioners reported to the House of Commons in 1856 work was then continuing in only seven parishes.[24] All the fields subject to tithe are listed in the apportionment under the names of their owners, together with their names, acreages and land use. The fields can be located on the ground by matching up the numbers entered on the apportionment with those written on the accompanying large-scale maps. The apportionments were originally bound in with the maps but most have subsequently been detached and filed separately. Three sets were made.[25] The originals are now deposited at the PRO at Kew, and the parochial and diocesan copies are to be found wherever the documents in the respective archives are placed. The PRO and the Tithe Redemption Office, Barrington Road, Durrington-on-Sea, Sussex, possess microfilm sets.

The awards not only list conventional farmland but also note a range of land uses such as woodlands, parks and plantations. Hop gardens, orchards and market gardens were carefully recorded as these might carry an extra rent charge. These are often represented on the map with a special symbol to facilitate identification.[26] The awards can be compared with estate surveys and valuations but normally they have the added advantage of containing information on land belonging to all owners in the parish.

Extra information can be found in the tithe files which contain material collected by the commissioners to help them assess the value of the tithes.[28] In some 6,000 tithe districts commutation was made by compulsory award. Here, the files usually contain the draft award, the minutes of meetings called by the assistant commissioners and any notes that they might have made. The contents of these files vary in quality, depending upon the attitude of individual officials, as well as upon the extent to which the documents were later weeded out. In another 6,740 districts an award was made after an agreement had been arrived at between the parties concerned. For such places the official had to submit a written report, and to help him (and to save time) printed forms were published. Two basic types were used, one to be employed in mainly arable areas and the other in pastoral districts.[28]

Unfortunately, the tithe files have been under-used, perhaps because no copies were made and the documents have to be examined at the PRO. Many describe the local farming system in great detail. Improvements were specifically noted – the appearance or otherwise of turnips was commonly used as an indication of 'progressive' agriculture. Assistant commissioners were often asked to give value judgements on the general quality of farming in the district. On the 'arable' forms they were specifically asked to observe instances of 'high' and 'low' farming as this would affect the amount of tithe paid. As can be seen in Appendix 7, the files give much incidental detail. At Laindon (Essex) the soil was particularly difficult to work. It was 'a stiff hungry clay soil, very cloddy, requiring to be ploughed five or six times . . . and in dry seasons as many as eight times'.[29] At Mortlake (Surrey) the long-established market gardening industry, based upon a plentiful supply of manure from the capital, is reflected in the assistant commissioner's comments. The soil, he found, had been 'rendered perfectly artificial by the constant application of manure, showing not a vestige of its original formation.[30]

Clearly the source is an extremely valuable one, but agrarian historians should not use it in an uncritical fashion. Information on crops, which were subject to the great tithe, tends to be fuller than that on animals, whilst acreages, yields and numbers of livestock were often mere estimates. At Chippenham (Wilts.) one of the assistant commissioners, Benjamin Braddock, 'got the number of cows he saw, and added 15 per cent for those not seen'.[31] With care, however, the material can be quantified. The relative importance of individual crops in a particular area, for instance, can be represented on separate choropleth maps, that is maps showing the acreage of each crop as a percentage of the total arable land. Distribution maps of animals can also be made, as either a series of dots or a ratio of the number of animals to a given acreage of grass- and meadowland.[32]

For a number of counties additional information on the state of agriculture in the mid nineteenth century can be obtained as a result of the government's renewed interest in agricultural statistics. In 1854 it voted for a grant of £13,000 to be spent on gathering information on farming in 11 selected counties. The action take was an experimental one, and as parliament wished to see the results of it the survey took the form of a report. The original statistics are therefore to be found among the sessional papers of the House of Commons: B.P.P. Reports by Poor Law Inspectors on Agricultural Statistics (England) House of Commons Sessional Papers 1854–5, Cd. 1928. The counties involved consisted of Berkshire, Breconshire, Denbighshire, Hampshire, Leicestershire, Norfolk, Shropshire, Suffolk, Wiltshire, Worcestershire and the West Riding of Yorkshire and include examples of most of the major farming types in the country.[33] The 1854 returns are more comprehensive than the returns of 1801 and contain details of grassland and waste and information on livestock as well as on crops. They therefore provide valuable evidence of the progress of high farming in these counties by that date and the ways in which farmers pursuing different forms of agriculture developed their enterprises. Apart from following such themes as the development of new crops and rotations, local historians can examine other aspects of land use such as ley farming and the watering of meadows. When the livestock figures are added in, integrated stock-crop regimes typical of high farming practice are often revealed. The cattle-corn economy of Leicestershire is a case in point. In other areas the figures indicate variations in animal husbandry – dairy farming in north Shropshire or grazing in the Market Harborough district of Leicestershire, for example.

Traditionally, the returns have been treated with some suspicion because of their assumed shortcomings. However, they have recently been rehabilitated by J. Philip Dodd, who has used them as the basis for a number of papers on farming in England in the mid nineteenth century. Some of the articles have appeared in county transactions and others in regional journals like *Midland History* and *Southern History*. In an article in the *Agricultural History Review*, 35, ii (1987) he discusses the value of the source in general, concluding that a 'detailed analysis of all the factors involved makes it possible to affirm that the statistics for the 1854 returns are a viable source of assessment of contemporary land use'. It must be borne in mind that the returns were based upon the Poor Law Union and as the units could be quite large (comprising a number of parishes), the figures represent an average which might mask considerable local variation. This deficiency cannot be overcome but, as in any comparative analysis, one needs to reduce the material to a common base. Dodd suggests that arable and livestock densities per thousand acres should be worked out and the findings plotted on a map.

Further statistics can be used to examine the changes that occurred in agriculture at a local level as the period of prosperity gave way to one of depression in the last quarter of the nineteenth century. A new set of figures, known as the Agricultural Returns, were first collected in 1866, prompted by the government's concern over the outbreak of cattle plague the previous year and its impact upon livestock numbers.[34] This time officers of the Inland Revenue undertook the work, and the figures, which continued to be taken on an annual basis to the present day, were published by the Statistical Department of the Board of Trade. When the Board of Agriculture was created in 1889 as a result of the Agriculture Act, responsibility for the collection of the statistics was transferred to it from the Board of Trade. Parish summaries for the years to 1963 have been deposited in the PRO at Kew among the records of the Ministry of Agriculture, Fisheries and Food, but unrestricted access is available only for material up to 1917. To look at later returns researchers have to sign a form undertaking not to extract information relating to an area with fewer than three holdings.[35]

When the returns were first taken, two lists were made; in March numbers of cattle, sheep and pigs in each parish were counted, whilst in June the acreage devoted to various crops was recorded.[36] Thereafter, the figures were collected at the same time, on 25 June each year. The earliest returns are somewhat unreliable – as ever, many farmers were wary about disclosing details of their business and the figures often under-represent the actual situation on the ground. Until 1917 the information was offered voluntarily, gaps being filled by estimates made by the collecting officers. Gradually, however, teething troubles were overcome, opposition decreased, and the returns became more comprehensive. Moreover, as the number of categories was enlarged and existing ones subdivided, it becomes possible to examine closely the type of farming being practised locally and thereby to refine the picture of farming regions.

Apart from recording new crops like mangolds and cabbages, the returns enable the local historian to see how far an earlier generation of crops – turnips and potatoes, for instance – had spread. Evidence on grassland management – the use of rotational grasses, pastures and fallows – can also be obtained. The imprint of the agricultural depression of the last quarter of the nineteenth century can clearly be seen in the figures. As the prices of corn and wool fell by the greatest amount, there was a noticeable movement away from mixed farming towards livestock husbandry in many villages. The trend is reflected in the laying down of a considerable acreage of arable land to grass and in the growth in the size of cattle herds. In Albrighton (Shrops.), for instance, the fallow and crop acreage fell from $1,420\frac{1}{2}$ acres in 1867 to 1,151 acres in 1907, whilst at the same time grassland increased from $1,146\frac{1}{2}$ acres to $1,866\frac{1}{2}$ acres.[37] The acreage of wheat, the grain most adversely affected, dropped from 492 acres to $174\frac{1}{2}$ acres. Barley did not suffer to the same extent, doubtless because of its use as a malt corn and a fodder crop. This source has obviously been well quarried by agrarian historians writing on the agriculture of the late nineteenth and early twentieth centuries, and a number of works have been produced using the returns.

An indication of the situation at the end of this period of depression can also be seen in the surveys of landed property drawn up as a result of the Lloyd George's reform of the land tax in 1910 (the Finance (1909–10) Act). Although short-lived (the land clauses were replaced by the Finance Act of 1920), the Act created a valuable archive of material and one which deserves to be better known.[38] To administer the Act, England and Wales were divided into four divisions (Scotland was organized separately), each under the control of a superintending valuer. The divisions were split up into districts, perhaps a whole county, under the charge of district valuers. Within the districts 'income tax parishes' were adopted as the basic unit of valuation, and these consisted of one or more civil parishes. Each 'parish' had a land valuation officer, normally an existing assessor of income tax, that is a local man with considerable knowledge of the area.

The main records include valuation books, which record the details of each hereditament (unit of occupancy) and give information on owner and occupier, together with land use and the extent of the property. This information was originally written out by the landowners on a form known as Form 4-Land. Among the other documents are the field books which normally contain data on one hundred hereditaments, with four pages being allocated to each property. On large estates, however, a separate file might have been kept. These documents contain details of the valuation and often give good descriptions of the property and occasionally a sketch map too. Forms 37-Land indicate the income tax parish and reference number of each hereditament, its address and exact acreage, as well as the name of the occupier. Because these forms are later in date than the valuation books, they sometimes reveal changes in land use. In many cases, schedules were attached to the forms, recording land use field by field. There are also marked up Ordnance Survey maps, two from each district office, one used for reference purposes and the other as a working copy.

Clearly, the source is an important one but it has not been fully used, partly because they have only been available for public consultation since 1979 and partly because the archive has been fragmented. In the past, moreover, their value has not always been recognized. The PRO offered the valuation books and the Forms 37-Land to local repositories in 1979, but they were not all taken. Tragically, many Forms 37-Land were destroyed in the mistaken belief that the material they contained merely duplicated that entered in the valuation books. County record offices also have examples of Forms 4-Land, having been given them by the district valuation office of the Inland Revenue. Others are still in those offices. The permanent sets of Ordnance Survey maps were retained by the district offices, where they can be found today, though it is intended eventually to transfer them to the PRO. The working copies were offered to local record offices in 1968 but, once more, the take-up around the country was uneven.

Later in the twentieth century, in the 1930s, the Land Utilization Survey under the direction of Dudley Stamp began to produce accounts of land use in various parts of the country. These surveys often use older material like the tithe awards to make comparisons with the past, and this adds interest to the work. Recently, the survey, now based at King's College, London, has been working towards the production of a land use map of Britain. Maps of areas already covered are available for inspection by *bona fida* students and can be used to indicate developments over the past few years. For the most up-to-date information the reader is advised to look over the hedge.

From the point of view of local administration, changes that occurred in the early modern period became more pronounced after the mid eighteenth century. The manor court continued to decline as its work was increasingly being taken over by the parish vestry. Of course, circumstances varied. At Wimbledon (Surrey) the manor court retained its vitality into the nineteenth century, and the rolls contain much of interest to agricultural historians. The vestry books, on the other hand, hardly mention the subject.[39] In contrast, at Ewell, another Surrey parish, the vestry was the dominant influence.[40] By the end of the nineteenth century, however, the authority of the parish vestry had diminished as well and with it the value of its records. After the local Government Act of 1894, which established parish councils, very little administrative work remained.[41]

At the county level changes in local government had already taken place. An act of 1888 established elected county- and county-borough councils, and these bodies assumed many of the administrative functions of the quarter sessions.[42] To facilitate the council in its work, numerous sub-committees were set up, several of which dealt with agricultural matters. Some of these committees were concerned with ordinary farming business, but others were created to deal with specific issues raised by parliamentary legislation – control of infectious diseases, allotments and smallholding, drainage and afforestation, for instance. The actual pattern varied from county to county and was complicated by the amalgamation and fragmentation of committees over time. In the county record office, where the records are to be found, there may be a flow chart to assist the archivists in the organization of the material that has come in. In Shropshire the earliest agricultural sub-committee was set up in 1889 and had power to deal with infected animals. An Allotment Committee was formed in 1891 with responsibility for local government allotments and smallholdings. In 1919 an Agricultural Committee was established to oversee a number of aspects of farming, and between 1948 and 1959 its work was extended to include land drainage and the control of animal disease. Other committees dealt with afforestation and rivers.[43]

In general, the documentation comprises minute books and ledgers, accounts and maps and plans, though other classes of material survive too. Many counties have complete runs of material, but, because of the sheer bulk of the archive, sampling may have taken place. For the local historian the records provide valuable evidence of agricultural developments in the county over the past century, especially in such spheres as agricultural education and the application of science to farming. They may be less helpful about the changes that have occurred at the local level for there is no certainty that a specific parish will appear in the documents. Researchers should sample one or two books to gain an impression of the material they contain, perhaps concentrating on years when changes are known to have occurred or on those which are significant to developments in agriculture in general.

In wartime the work of these committees was taken over by specially appointed bodies who had the responsibility of running agriculture in the shires.[44] These were known as the War Agricultural Executive Committees (WAECs). They were particularly concerned with increasing the supply of home produced food and are full of references to ways in which it could be achieved. In the First World War measures were introduced with the aim of bringing about a rapid improvement in arable cultivation, including the planting of wheat on land normally sown with oats and potatoes and the reclamation of at least one million acres to accommodate the latter two crops.[45] Such drastic action caused tremendous upheaval; many farmers had little or no experience of arable farming and the extension of the area of cultivation led to serious logistical problems too. The task of the committees was to advise farmers, to deal with problems of organization and to ensure an adequate supply of essential items like seed, labour, equipment and power. The officials inevitably met a certain amount of resentment from farmers, who viewed them as outsiders whose intrusion was both unwelcome and unwarranted. In the Second World War the same pattern re-emerged; indeed, the authorities seem to have looked back to the proceedings during the earlier conflict for guidance on the course of action to be followed.

Summary

The growing volume of documentation for the modern period makes it easier for local historians to find information on farming practices for their own community. To the classes of record which continue from an earlier date, new sources are added. Many of these are of an official nature which, because of the growing desire to learn more about the state of agriculture in the country, provide direct evidence of farming methods and systems. In spite of the difficulties in using this material and the problems to be faced when interpreting it, these sources mark a qualitative improvement in the standard of documentation available for research. Moreover, they allow comparisons to be made over time, enabling agrarian historians to assess the local impact of major fluctuations in agriculture at a national level.

Chapter Four

THE IMPACT OF FARMING UPON THE LANDSCAPE

The landscape of England today is almost completely an artificial one for very few places have remained untouched by the hand of man.[1] Historically, farming has been a major agent in this process of change. As more land was needed, farmers extended the area of cultivation onto the wastes, burning the undergrowth, felling the trees and draining the fens and coastal marshes. It was not an inexorable process, however. Spurts of activity, coinciding with times of rising population, alternated with periods of stagnation when the margin of cultivation retreated, allowing the land left outside it to be reclaimed by nature. Thus, population pressure in late Roman England and in the high Middle Ages led to the establishment of numerous communities on marginal land, many of which were abandoned in the subsequent demographic crisis.[2]

Sometimes, land was enclosed directly from the waste, at other times it was added as strips and furlongs to the open fields. The development of open field systems is still a controversial issue, but it is clear that the movement varied over time and place and that we cannot be dogmatic about the issues involved.[3] Land brought into cultivation, by whatever means, was subject to further change too. Open field strips were enclosed, earlier in some places than in others, and today they survive, much modified, in a mere handful of places. Fields altered in size and shape as farmers divided or amalgamated their closes. Recently, the trend has been towards larger fields, and farmers, grubbing up hedges in pursuit of agricultural efficiency, are in many areas recreating the open landscape of a past age.

Documentary research of this topic should always be combined with field work and there should be constant interaction between the two. On the one hand, readers ought to assimilate the information contained in documents before venturing into the landscape, as this will help them untangle the various layers of visual material presented to them. On the other, a particular observation – the alignment of a lane, the pattern of the fields or a diverted watercourse – might invite questions which only research into the documents can answer. This joint approach was advocated with particular vigour by Professor Hoskins, and for examples of what can be done his book, *Fieldwork in Local History*, is recommended.[4]

The recent interest in hedge-dating indicates one area in which an attempt has been made to integrate the two. Hedges are important historical features in the landscape, revealing, among other things, farming practices, land use and field systems through the ages. If they could be dated with any degree of precision, many aspects of agricultural development could be more effectively studied. The basic principle, first put forward by Dr Max Hooper in the mid 1960s, proposes that there is a connexion between the age of a hedge and the number of species it contains. Using documentary sources to ascertain the age of particular hedges and correlating his findings with the result of fieldwork, he suggested that, in general, hedges were colonized by a new species every hundred years.[5]

Many local historians have used this formula to look at hedges in their own area but if they do so in an uncritical manner, their conclusions are likely to be inaccurate. The method does have serious limitations, a fact noted by Dr Hooper himself, and these relate to differences in the origin of hedges and regional variations in geography and hedge management. What is needed is a more sophisticated technique of classification which resolves the problems of the original method and which can be used in all parts of the country.[6]

The Anglo-Saxon period

For material on the pre-Conquest landscape the reader will have to rely upon the work of others. Much information concerning the period is derived from archaeological and place-name evidence, disciplines which require specialist training. Under no circumstance, for example, should the non-expert start digging up the interesting lumps and bumps of a suspected deserted village or go prospecting for field boundaries shown up as crop marks on aerial photographs. This course of action will only disturb the site and destroy vital evidence. Anyone wanting to get involved in this aspect of research should approach organizations doing work in the field – the archaeological unit of the county council, a university or a local/county history society – and volunteer their help at any excavation being planned or undertaken.

The enthusiastic amateur does have a role to play, however. By keeping a watching brief on the locality, especially when fields are being ploughed, trenches dug, or roads constructed, he or she can bring to the attention of a competent archaeologist any significant features seen (without moving any finds). Recent research indicates that many settlement sites were not fixed until after the Norman Conquest, and evidence of the predecessors of today's communities may therefore be found away from the present site.

Of the documentary sources, Anglo-Saxon charters, which deal with grants of land, provide some clues about the nature of the landscape.[7] In particular, they describe the boundaries of the properties being given. Most of the charters are available in transcript. The earliest ones tend merely to give generalized topographical information but do reveal a regulated landscape, one that was organized into a hierarchy of units and which was being exploited for farming (and for other activities). In time, the charters become more numerous and more informative, showing in greater detail the expansion onto the wastes and differences in land-use. At Hawling in the Cotswolds an undated charter, probably of the late tenth century, indicates the existence of large areas of woodland and open pasture and, after their bounds have been traced, by elimination the location of the village's arable land.[8] Unfortunately, the usefulness of the charters as a source is hampered by doubts about their dating and authenticity, their limited number (only some 800 in all) and their uneven distribution both chronologically and geographically. Moreover, as they list points in a line, they provide little evidence of the landscape within the estate.

Interpreting the names mentioned in the charters, moreover, is a matter for the expert. The obvious meaning is not necessarily the correct one – it is often totally wrong – and the unskilled amateur can easily be led astray. As Margaret Gelling observes in her admirable introduction to the subject, *Signposts to the Past* (Dent, London, 1978), 'it is therefore important at the outset to ask people who have had no special competence in the history of the English language to accept special guidance about the meaning of place names before building a theory on a supposed etymology'. Even experts disagree, mistakes are made and theories overturned, perhaps because interpretations were not checked in the field. The local historian, ironically, is well placed to decide, for instance, if the letters h-a-m at the end of a village's name refers to 'ham' (village) or to 'hamm' (meadow). For guidance the reader should consult the relevant county volume of the English Place Name Society.

The Post-Norman Conquest period

The first nationwide source of topographical information that we possess is the Domesday Book. Because it gives details of land use, it tells us about the nature of the local landscape. Clearly, areas with a high proportion of arable land do not look the same as those containing larger proportions of waste or woodland. Professor Darby, in particular, has made good use of the material, publishing his work in a number of regional studies under the general title of the Domesday Geography of England.[9] By plotting on a map the various features mentioned in the survey, he was able to highlight differences around the country. The pattern of woodland, for instance, is an interesting one, though it should be noted that the woods were not always located in the manors under which they were entered. In the Weald of Surrey large amounts of woodland were recorded for manors which lay just outside the area but which had common rights in it. In Warwickshire, on the other hand, the distinction between the well-wooded Forest of Arden half of the county and the more open champion half is plain to see.[10]

Surveys and extents, because they deal with individual estates, provide a more detailed account. When analysing the figures, one should, of course, take care, given the vagaries of medieval measurement. As noted in Chapter 1, the demesne is the best documented part of the estate. Apart from noting the acreage of open-field and enclosed land belonging to the demesne, the documents also mention other topographical features such as parks, woodlands, ponds and wastes. A number of manorial extents can be found among the piles of miscellanous inquisitions deposited in the PRO in Chancery Lane. These records, drawn up to accompany specific enquiries, have been calendared and indexed for the years 1219 to 1399.[11] Similar material appears in the Hundred Rolls of 1279. Information on non-demesne holdings can be found in terriers. Some refer to freehold estates but many of them deal with all the land of a township or manor. They are often very detailed, describing land belonging to tenants strip by strip and close by close.

Whereas surveys and extents provide snapshots of places at irregular (and perhaps widely spaced) intervals, other manorial documents such as court rolls and accounts offer a more regular, if variable, source of information and help to pinpoint the time when changes occurred. Surrenders of property made at the court baron might refer to closes taken out of the common or to strips in the open fields. Additional topographical material can be obtained from those entries in the court rolls which deal with the regulation of the open fields and commons or which record offences against the local by-laws. Small-scale encroachment from the waste is particularly well-documented as it was frequently carried out without licence and was therefore brought to the attention of the court. If licensed, it would also appear on the rolls. Examples of enclosure of open field strips can also be found. Account rolls, too, contain information of a topographical nature. New assarts were often listed separately on the rolls, whilst the expansion of farm land is reflected in an increase in the income noted there and in rentals. If the work was carried out at the lord's command, labour costs incurred in the improvement will be recorded.

Manorial collections also include contemporary deeds and charters, either in the form of individual documents or as entries in cartularies. In general, these post-Conquest records are more easy to use and interpret than those which belong to the Anglo-Saxon period. Unlike the earlier ones, which may have been falsified and modified and only transcribed into cartularies one or two centuries after the original grant, these deeds were normally set down immediately. In this respect, they reflect the growing use of the written record that occurred in the twelfth and thirteenth centuries.[12] Many of the grants were small scale, and therefore the deeds had to locate the parcels of land more precisely on the ground. Names and acreages were often given and the open field strips distin-guished from closes. The furlongs in which the strips lay were noted and perhaps their abuttals too. Sometimes, the process of change can be seen in the documents, as in the exchange of strips that was made prior to enclosure. Other improvements can be picked out as well. In the Lincolnshire fens the task of reclaiming the land from the sea is indicated in the many thousands of charters and deeds entered into monastic cartularies of the area.[13]

The great increase in the number of field and other minor names which can be obtained from post-Conquest deeds is a bonus for the local historian, especially as the descriptive elements in them are less confusing. Clearance of woodland, for instance, is indicated by names such as 'ridding' and 'stocking', whilst the existence of former open field arable is suggested by the elements 'land', 'butt', 'flatt' and 'furlong'. For reference, readers should look at John Field's book, *English Field Names: A Dictionary*. The more recent county volumes of the English Place Name Society give greater space to minor place names, but what is really needed is more handbooks like H. D. G. Foxall's *Shropshire Field Names*.[14] Readers could help by compiling a register of names, beginning with those of the present day, obtainable from local farmers, and then working back through documents such as surveys of various sorts, manor court rolls, deeds and accounts.

Finally, the records of forest administration should be consulted for they contain much of topographical interest (though one would not want to start a study with this source for the documents are very difficult to read). In the Middle Ages a large amount of land was subject to forest law – in the reign of Henry II as much as one-third of the country may have been deemed 'forest'. Not all of the land was necessarily wooded (though much of it was), 'forest' being a legal rather than a botanical term, but the administration of the law had a profound effect on the landscape. Animals could not be taken without licence, assarts were forbidden and restrictions were placed upon farming.

The extent of the forest can be gauged from various perambulations which were made, while many presentments recorded on the forest rolls were for infringements of the forest law. Most commonly these were for illegal grazing and encroachment and they suggest pressures on land. In spite of the ban on assarting in the forest, encroachements were constantly being made, notably at the time of rising population in the twelfth and thirteenth centuries. At Rushock (Worcs.) in 1262 Henry Sturmy paid a fine of 3s. 4d. for an old assart he had made in the forest of Feckenham. At the same time inhabitants from the neighbouring parishes of

Chaddesley Corbet, Elmbridge, Upton Warren and Dodford with Grafton were punished for similar offences.[16] In total, the area encroached upon could be considerable. In a regard of the Forest of Dean in 1282 fines for old assarts amounted to £98 5s. 9d. and for new ones £238 17s 0d. Of this sum, the abbot of Tintern had to pay £168 for 352 acres taken in by his predecessor.[17]

The early modern period

The estate

The most important feature of the early modern period was the burgeoning use of maps. Maps had been produced in the Middle Ages but, as medieval surveys had been largely concerned with valuation rather than measurement, greater emphasis was given to the written survey. Some examples are known but they are rare and not very accurate.[18] In the period after the mid sixteenth century a cartographical revolution occurred, as advances in mathematics and geometry, improvements in surveying implements and the growth of a professional class of surveyors combined to improve the quality of maps and the associated surveys. The best examples, moreover, do not merely provide an accurate and detailed cartographical record but, with their decorated borders, compass roses and heraldic devices, are exquisite works of art.[19]

As the maps mainly relate to rural estates, they are of particular value to students of agricultural topography. For the first time we can see the landscape as it was viewed by contemporaries, though the accuracy of the individual maps has to be assessed. They were not all of the same standard, and crudely drawn examples continued to be made. Thus, a map showing the division of Tilstock Park (Shrops.) in c. 1600 between farmers Green, Chawner and Gregory consists of a rough plan of the area with the partitions indicated by the use of thick, murky colours.[20] In time, especially after c. 1700, the overall standard of map making rose as equipment improved and the number of professional surveyors increased. The reader should still take care, however, for surveyors varied widely in competence and honestly, and wherever possible the information should be checked against other maps and documents and in the field.[21]

The patrons mainly comprised substantial landowners who required an accurate record of their estates, often scattered across several counties. Numerous maps were made for a specific purpose – when an enclosure or an exchange of lands was being contemplated or when a property was in dispute or being earmarked for sale. Landlords also had them drawn up to reap the benefits from having the estate surveyed and mapped afresh. For communities which form part of a large estate there should therefore be at least one map (and probably one or two others) covering the area. Local historians should remember, however, that, as many of the maps solely depict land belonging to the estate, they may gain only a partial view of their communities. According to J. B. Harley only one map in ten covers a whole parish.[22] The comprehensiveness of a particular map will clearly be related to the amount of land held locally by the individual proprietor, and as a result closed parishes with a single dominant landowner are likely to be the best served.

Many estate maps were designed on a large scale, ranging from 10 to 40 inches to the mile, and this allows for the inclusion of even minor details. As J. B. Harley has observed, 'an aggregate list of the features shown on estate maps is well nigh a complete inventory of the rural landscape, though the local historian must not expect to encounter all, or even a large proportion, in any one map.'[23] Field boundaries should be shown, together with their names and acreages, and perhaps (with a colour code) the use to which they were being put. Occasionally, the nature of the soil is given. Settlements and roads, as well as more specialized features, might also be depicted.

Estate maps, therefore, graphically illustrate the nature of the local landscape at a particular time. Those depicting open-field communities might show the outlines of the great open arable fields or even the location of each strip, as at Padbury (Bucks.) in 1591 and at Weston Pinkney (Notts.) in 1593.[24] In other communities, where open field farming was less important, maps reveal a more fragmented landscape with strips interspersed with closes. Evidence of piecemeal enclosure might be apparent in the number of closes and in the ragged outline of the residual open fields. Consolidated blocks of strips, perhaps several acres in size, suggest that further enclosure was about to be made. Other maps were drawn up specifically to record enclosure of land – either open-field strips or areas of waste – and the partition of land among a number of new holdings.

Many maps are accompanied by reference books which can be termed surveys, terriers and field books, and these should be examined together. Other surveys were made independently, in effect continuing the medieval tradition of the written record. Manorial surveys were still common in early-modern England, especially up to *c.* 1700 when they tended to be replaced by valuations.[25] They become more informative too, as details of the land farmed by the tenants was often included in them. This may take the form of a generalized account of land use on each holding but it might also provide extra information, distinguishing between open field and enclosed land and giving names and acreages of strips and closes. Commons and wastes, as in medieval surveys, are particularly well documented.

Surveys are more numerous than maps, and on large estates at least there should be series of them to help the researchers chart any developments that occurred. At Rushock (Worcs.) six surveys of all or part of the Wolverhampton Grammar School estate were made between 1572 and 1772.[26] The survey of 1624 deals solely with the demesne, whilst that of 1624 lists only the fields of the home farm, although it does include the names of the tenants and the rents they were paying. The other four surveys, however, encompass the whole estate, covering some three-quarters of the parish. Those of 1572 and 1772 were field books accompanying maps, though the existence of the 1572 map is known only because of an entry in the records of the Merchant Tailors' company which accounts for money paid out for a case for it.[27] Topographically, they show fluctuations in the size of individual closes, as fields were amalgamated or divided up, and the continuing break-up of the open fields.

Other medieval estate and manorial records – accounts, court rolls and deeds – carry on into the early modern period, providing the same kind of information as they had done before. Presentments were still being made at the manor court of encroachments on the waste and in the open fields, whilst descriptions of customary land surrendered at the court baron were written onto the rolls. Similar material also appears in deeds of various sorts. From the sixteenth century onwards, however, there tend to be far more leases among the documentation, as this form of letting out land became more widespread. Some give merely an outline description of the property, but others include details of every plot of land demised. As with other deeds, the data can be used to calculate the ratio between open field and enclosed land and, where a series of leases for the same property exist, the changing relationship between the two. The documents may also show assarting of the wastes by the abridgement of common rights there, the provision of alternative grazing grounds or the annexation of the land so enclosed to individual farms.

Estate and manorial accounts, like their medieval counterparts, list payments for work done on projects that had an effect on the landscape – paling the park, hedging and ditching around the fields, grubbing up hedges and felling trees, and draining ponds and marshes. Estate correspondence is even more diverse. Among the items discussed in letters written by Daniel Eaton, the land steward of the third Earl of Cardigan, to his master in the early eighteenth century are the management of the fields, woods and parks, the enclosure of the open fields and commons, exchanges of land, the use of lime and other fertilizers and the construction and repair of roads.[28]

One important technological development of the late sixteenth and seventeenth centuries that can be revealed by a combination of records is the practice of floating water meadows. Using a system of dams and channels, streams were diverted over upland meadows in winter, imitating the flooding of riverside meadows. In this way, not only was the ground protected from frost but fertility was also enhanced through the depositing of silt and other organic materials. Surveys might refer to this innovation. In a marginal note written in a survey of Eyton (Herefs.), taken in January 1582/3, the following comment was made: 'Memorandum that this oxepasture of Somergilles may be overflowen in the winter in time of grete floods by letting in the flodd in iii or iiii places above the bridge and owt of the pasture next above, so the renes may be filled and the pasture yerely amended.'[29]

Agreements were also made between various parties, and these survive in the form of indentures. In 1697 Henry Davenport of Hallon (Shrops.) made an agreement with John Harwood D.D. concerning the use of the River Worfe for such a purpose. According to the document, they agreed to make several pools and dams on their lands and maintain floodgates on the river 'for the Convenience of floting and carrying the water from the said Flud gate over the Land of

Each of them'.[30] The work, moreover, gave employment to labourers on the estate. In the accounts of the Corbetts of Acton Reynalds (Shrops.) is a reference to the payment of £1 to John Bishop for drowning the meadows at Little Withiford.[31] Because of the expense involved, most of the early schemes were carried out by large landowners. Nonetheless, as the improvement offered such obvious benefits, some communities agreed amongst themselves to share the cost. Records of such agreements should appear in either the manor court rolls or the vestry minute books.

Most of this estate material will be found in the muniment rooms of landed families, in solicitors' chambers or county record offices. Documents relating to Crown property, however, have been deposited in the PRO Chancery Lane, as have those drawn up in connexion with the work of the Augmentations Office. Surveys were taken of all properties that came into the Court's hands, and the information entered onto in them is similar to that contained in other records of the same kind. Thus, a survey of the land of the late monastery of Bellaland in Yorkshire, taken in 1538, gives details of each field, including their names and acreages and often their land use.[32] The archive is an extremely varied one and well worth investigating, though, typically, researchers have to slog their way through a number of different lists for local references.[33]

The Parliamentary surveys of the mid seventeenth century, mostly incorporated in the same archive,[34] follow a similar format to the earlier ones. Woods are particularly well documented not only because they added to the value of the estate but also because Parliament wanted supplies of timber for the navy. The survey of Enfield Park in 1650, for instance, states that there were 7,093 oaks and hornbeams there, many very old and some of great size. Including the unknown number of smaller hornbeams, whitethorns and maples, the timber in the park was worth £1,762 2s. 6d. There were 397 other timber trees that had not been assessed, having been earmarked for the navy. On Enfield Chase 2,500 timber trees, worth £1 each, were growing, along with others not valued because they too were designated for naval use. On the waste of the manor of Enfield were a number of small trees reckoned by the commissioners to be worth £13.[35]

Other records

For information on communities not covered by estate records readers can first of all turn to the topographical accounts of the period, which may give a general description of the area. According to John Leland, in the 1540s 'suche parte of Leirestershir as is lying by south and est is champaine and hath little wood. And suche parte of Leircestershir as lyith by west and north hath much wodde'.[36] At a local level, county histories or, where they exist, parochial ones may provide other details. Richard Gough's account of the parish of Myddle (Shrops.), written *c.* 1700, is full of topographical references. Myddlewood Common, he noted, had been 'formerly a famous wood of timber; there is a great part of itt inclosed, some into tenements . . . severall persons have cottages on the common, and one or two peices inclosed to every cottage . . . Severall pieces of this Common have beene inclosed and added to tenements in Myddle and Marton.'[37]

Glebe terriers are a particular good source for filling in the gaps. Because they run in series, they indicate the progress of enclosure – at a single stroke in many open-field villages or in a more piecemeal fashion elsewhere. Clearly, however, the glebe was not a typical property. Dr Yelling has observed that in areas of piecemeal enclosure the glebe often tended to possess a much greater proportion of open-field land than the other holdings.[38] Professor Beresford, in an article on glebe terriers, suggests the following criteria.[39] Firstly, if the parson had strips, so did the ordinary villager; similarly, if the parson had a mixture of strips and closes, the same pattern would tend to be repeated on the other farms; finally if the parson had only closes, the other villagers may have had the same or they may still have had strips.

The value of the glebe terriers lies in the fact that they relate to a known holding over a period of time and that they often reflect changes that were occurring more generally in the community. At Highley (Shrops.) the whole community was involved in enclosure, for in a glebe terrier of February 1625/6 it was stated that the parishioners, all freeholders, had exchanged and enclosed the open fields for 'theyre more commodious use'.[40] As a result, the incumbent, 'for the good of the church and with the consent of his ordinary and patron', joined in. In Shropshire in general, the break up of the open fields was a protracted affair, and the terriers reflect the slow pace of change, with successive documents showing the piecemeal enclosure of the fields.[41] At Kinnersley upon the Weald Moors, for instance, the terrier of 1612 (see Appendix 6) shows much of the land in strips. Their enclosure can be traced in subsequent terriers, though they span 118 years.

Another ecclesiastical source which provides topographical information is the class of material dealing with tithe disputes. Many disputes occurred when land was enclosed or drained because, as it rose in value, the tithe owner naturally sought to take his share. In a Yorkshire case of 1560 the tithe owner claimed not only tithe on cattle grazing on an enclosed moor but also an increment due because of its increased value. According to Michael Rawdon, farmer of the tithes of Rawdon Moor, the inhabitants had, as a result of this efforts, benefited from the provision of better pasture for their animals.[42]

Changes in the landscape, especially those brought about by enclosure and drainage, can be followed in the government's records too, in either the papers belonging to the various enclosure commissions it established or those of the equity courts. These documents can be examined in the PRO in Chancery Lane.[43] In Chancery hundreds of files exist which record the evidence given by local juries in response to the enclosure commissioners' request for information. Nonetheless, it is probably more convenient to study the work of the commissioners in the rolls of the court of Exchequer.[44] Even if cases were heard elsewhere, in Chancery, in King's Bench or at the assizes, the details (and verdict) were copied onto the Exchequer rolls because of the fiscal element inherent in the proceedings. In an appendix to his book *The Lost Villages of England*, Professor Beresford lists by county and year the enclosure cases enrolled in Exchequer between 1517 and 1565, together with the Exchequer roll number, as an aid to research. The results of the 1517–18 Commission, moreover, are largely in print, having been transcribed and published by I. S. Leadam in the *Domesday of Enclosures* (Royal Historical Society, London, 1897) and in three articles in the *Transactions of the Royal Historical Society* 1892–4.

The south and east Midlands were the areas most severely affected and the ones visited by the commissioners, and clearly local historians there will gain most from an examination of the records. However, the picture obtained will be only a partial one, for cases brought to court represent only a proportion of contemporary enclosing activity, either because evidence was suppressed or because it had taken place before the commissions' terms of reference began. Only 23 counties were dealt with by the 1517–18 enquiry, and the returns are incomplete. For 1548, documentation covered two counties, Warwickshire and Cambridgeshire, whilst the workings of the 1565 commission is represented by fragments of material from Buckinghamshire and Leicestershire. Evidence is more readily available for the seven Midlands counties surveyed in 1607 but it has many shortcomings and limitations, reflecting the difficulties of the commissioners' task.

Far more numerous were the private suits involving enclosure which can be found in the records of the equity courts (including those of Chancery and Exchequer) or in those of regional bodies like the Councils of the North, the West and the Marches of Wales. Chancery was a court of civil jurisdiction too and as such heard cases concerning property. Moreover, as disputes over enclosure might lead to rioting and looting, they could be sent to Star Chamber where such cases were dealt with. Others were heard in the court of Exchequer. As the witnesses had only a loose framework to which to adhere, the depositions taken locally contain much incidental information.

As was the case in property disputes in general, the documents might include maps, drawn up to illustrate the various points in contention. In the late sixteenth and early seventeenth centuries a number of maps were made to accompany the series of disputes that dogged the progress of enclosure and drainage in the Weald Moors, a low-lying area of fen in east Shropshire.[45] Although of variable quality – the worst are mere free hand sketches with little or no carto-graphical skill and were biased towards the point of view of one or other of the parties – they are invaluable as a source of topographical information on the area.

Even if enclosure was carried out by agreement, the participants often felt it necessary to obtain some form of legal sanction for the exchanges or assarts made. The device most commonly employed in the early modern period was the collusive Chancery suit,[46] although greater use was being made of private act of parliament by the early eighteenth century. In essence, the process involved a fictitious suit being brought to court in order to gain an agreed decision and thereby give it legal standing. The decrees contain much

additional information which may include considerable topographical detail.

The modern period

From what has been written so far, it is clear that improvement of the commons and wastes and the enclosure of the
open fields had had a long history before the period of
parliamentary enclosure. In some parts of the country the
open fields had already disappeared or were in full decline. If,
in these areas, parliamentary sanction was needed for land
improvement, it was largely for the purpose of bringing the
wastes into regular cultivation. Even in areas of open-field
farming like the east Midlands, a number of parishes had been
enclosed by the mid eighteenth century. Much work remained
to be done, however, and, as Dr Turner has written in his
book *English Parliamentary Enclosure* 'Parliamentary enclosure
was possibly the largest single aggregate landscape change
induced by man in an equivalent period of time.'[47] Circumstances varied between counties, however. In Oxfordshire
and Northamptonshire over 50 per cent of the land was
enclosed by act of parliament, whereas in Cornwall, Devon,
Essex, Kent and Sussex the amount was negligible.[48]

Topographically, the effect was related to the type of land
being enclosed and the acreage involved. Where the open
fields remained virtually intact, as they did in a large part of
central England, hundreds of acres, divided into thousands of
strips, were enclosed. Instead of an open landscape, largely
unbroken by any boundary, the scene was filled with regularly
shaped fields surrounded by hedges in which fruit and other
trees might be planted. When the enclosure commissioners
laid out these fields they had to give consideration to the lines
of communication. Major routeways normally followed the
same course as before (perhaps straightened), but minor roads
and tracks were often altered. Characteristically, commissioners' roads were straight, changing direction with right
angled bends.[49] They tended to be uniform in width and had
wide grass verges – sometimes the distance between hedges
measured 40 to 60 feet. As road-making techniques improved
in the early nineteenth century, the need to by-pass rutted and
boggy sections of road diminished, and verges became
narrower.

At the same time dramatic changes took place in other parts

of the country, notably in the North and West, where open fields were lacking but where there were large acreages of common land and waste. Before enclosure the scenery – woodland, fen, moor or heath – would have contrasted with that of open-field areas, but thereafter a similar landscape of hedged fields emerged. The most obvious difference lay in the mode of dividing the fields – drainage ditches in the fens and drystone walling on the upland moors. In many places, of course, the contrast was less noticeable, enclosing activity being limited to the tidying away of a decaying-open field system or to the improvement of a small common or green.

The process of enclosure took a number of years to complete. This time-lag reflected the complex and arduous task confronting the commissioners; surveying the fields, assessing the value of each owner's property, reorganizing the roads and drains, settling disputes and arriving at a final allotment were among the jobs that had to be done and they all required time and patience. An account of the deliberations and actions of the commissioners can be found in the minute books that were kept as a record of their meetings. Even after an act had been passed, more time elapsed before the full effect of the measure was seen. Ring fences or hedges soon appeared around individual allotments, but as the pressure on making internal divisions was not as great they were not dealt with so quickly. Sometimes, the award was only partially put into effect as expectations of the gains to be obtained from a particular measure fell. This illustrates the point that the mere existence of an award does not necessarily imply that all (or, indeed, any) of the land involved was enclosed at that time.

The awards themselves can be consulted in the original at the House of Lords Record Office or as copies given to the parish or (after 1792) enrolled by the Clerk of the Peace. The copies can normally be found in the county record office. Because, as a public record, an official copy was made (that is, 'enrolled'), the survival rate of this source of information is very good. The awards contain much of topographical interest. If open-field strips were being enclosed, the names and acreages of the parcels of land involved were given, together with their abuttals and location in the fields. Closes may also be included in the exchanges. Where commons and wastes were being dealt with, the acreages of the new allotments were noted.

A more immediate impression of change is conveyed by the

accompanying map or maps, even if they vary in scale, scope and detail. In areas where large-scale enclosure of the open fields occurred, the maps often show the lay-out of the entire parish and not merely the allotments. Some draft plans made by the commissioners survive, especially for the period after 1830, which, because they were drawn up in the initial stages of the process, show the pre-enclosure landscape. On the other hand, maps accompanying the enclosure of greens, small acreage of open-field land and even large commons tend merely to depict the actual area involved.[50]

Some indication of the amount of common land left in the country in the late nineteenth century can be gained from the census of common lands of 1873–4. The work was carried out by the Copyhold, Inclosure and Tithe Commissioners and was made at a time whe interest in the preservation of common land was growing. The return covers 292 foolscap pages and was made on a parochial basis. It is to be found among the other parliamentary papers in the House of Lords Records Office and has the reference number: BPP House of Commons, Paper 85, *A Return of Waste Lands – 1873* (1874). The material should be used with care because it was based solely on documents in the possession of the Commission and not on a survey in the field, and a considerable amount of guesswork was involved. What it does show, however, is that in 1873–4 a large acreage of common arable land remained and that much still had to be done in the subsequent period.[51]

Enclosure plans, by definition, provide evidence of changes in the landscape, but other enrolled plans give information too. Transport maps, especially those relating to river, canal and railway schemes, contain useful material.[52] The plans show the line of the route and a ribbon of land, perhaps one-quarter of a mile in width, on either side. Rennie's plan of the proposed Chelmer and Blackwater Navigation (1792–4), for instance, was drawn up to a scale of 6.6 inches to the mile and depicts in considerable detail the land up to 1 mile on either side of the river.[53] Plans of other public works such as the construction of docks contain similar information, though the land involved was a more compact block.

Tithe awards are another valuable source of information on topography. The maps were drawn up on a large, though variable, scale. They are accurate enough for the purposes of most local historians, even if only about 1,900, roughly one-sixth of the total, were designated as first class and given the commissioners' seal of approval. First-class maps were those that conformed to the specific standards set by Lieutenant Dawson, who had been given the task of working out the technical specification, namely maps at a scale of three chains to an inch (26.7 inches to a mile) constructed by a strict system of triangulation. Second-class maps included those that failed Dawson's tests and those that never aspired to that status. These maps, many of which were based on existing parish or estate maps, were not necessarily inferior but were debarred from consideration because the scale was not large enough.[54]

In many places the tithe award provides the first large-scale survey of a parish or township and gives a detailed picture of the landscape – land use, fields, hedgerows and commons, farms and farm buildings and roads and tracks. Open fields can be seen, many clearly on the point of disappearing but some still occupying a considerable area. Even if they had already been swept away, their former existence often survived in the shape of some of the fields and in the names given to them. The size and layout of farms can also be examined, utilizing the information listed in the owner and occupier columns of the apportionment. The tithe files should be looked at too. From the topographical point of view, they may describe the area concerned, the organization of the fields, the nature of the soil and general land use.

The early nineteenth century also saw the final stage in the development of the private county map.[55] Earlier cartographers like Saxton, Norden and Speed put in little topographical information, though parks were carefully marked, perhaps an indication of the social standing of the people who patronized them. From the mid eighteenth century, however, advances were made which were reflected in the work of mapmakers such as Rocque and Taylor. Scales varied from one-quarter of an inch to 2 inches to the mile (most commonly 1 inch) so that, whilst they cannot show all the information depicted on later large-scale Ordnance Survey maps, they are big enough to include some detail. In particular, they provide evidence in a generalized way of land use and enclosure over a large area, indicating settlements, fields, strips, parks, commons and woods. Moreover, as many early nineteenth century maps were drawn on a scale similar to that of earlier examples, an assessment of changes that had occurred in the landscape can be made.

It must be borne in mind when examining county maps that

as a class they are often difficult to date with precision and that there are defects in their provenance, comprehensiveness and accuracy. Even reputable mapmakers like the Greenwoods made use of existing maps. Earlier cartographers, not having the same advantage of Ordnance Survey triangulation data to assist them, were bound to be less accurate in their work, even if they did not deliberately distort or simplify the material. When Rocque's map, 'An Exact Survey of the City of London, Westminster . . . and the Country near Ten Miles Round' (1744–6) was compared with contemporary estate maps of Essex, many of the features were found to be 'untrustworthy' and the field boundaries 'largely fictitious'.

In southern England the early-nineteenth-century county maps coincided with the appearance of the first Ordnance Survey maps, also published in county sheets of 1 inch to the mile.[56] Comparisons can therefore be made concerning the evolution of the agricultural landscape. Land use can be discerned and the progress of enclosure measured, though, as no dates or field boundaries are given, only general observations can be made. Local historians will find the original surveyors' drawings, deposited in the Map Room of the British Museum, much more helpful since, unlike the published maps, they reflect conditions at the time that the survey was made. They were also drawn on a larger scale (2, 3 or 6 inches to the mile) and, as a result, include detailed topographical features such as field boundaries.,

For local study the larger-scale maps which become available from the mid-nineteenth century are more useful. For most purposes the 6-in. version is sufficient: it is on a manageable scale and covers an area at least the size of a parish, even if parishes being studied always seem to be located on the edge of two or more OS maps! Moreover, the 6-inch map, unlike the 25-inch one, gives contour lines. For particular detailed work the 25-inch map should be examined. All topographical features are shown to scale, acreages of fields are noted and for the first time delineated with complete accuracy.

Non-agricultural developments bulk large in comparisons between various editions – the growth of towns and suburbs and the development of industry, for instance – but changes in agricultural practice are also illustrated. Farmland continued to encroach upon woods, heaths and moors, though a growing appreciation of commonland as a public amenity and as sites of special scientific interest had slowed down the pace of change. Where the Forestry Commission operates the process is being reversed, even if the planting of acres of conifer trees in regimented rows hardly constitutes a recreation of an earlier landscape. Some areas of open-field farming appear on the first edition, only to disappear before later ones were made – on the North Downs the strips in parishes like Epsom and Leatherhead were not finally enclosed until the 1860s. Parkland, too, may have been converted into fields, if not buried under bricks and mortar. On the other hand, the modern trend towards larger fields is opening up the landscape and the disappearance of the hedgerows is a phenomenon that can readily be seen on the OS maps.

Valuable topographical information also appears in the boundary remarks books and accompanying sketch maps made as a result of the Ordnance Survey Act of 1841, which provided for the determination and marking out of boundaries to be included on the maps.[57] The boundaries were located in relation to physical features, some of which have subsequently disappeared, and thus the books preserve a record of an older landscape. Overall, the maps contain a wealth of detail and therefore deserve to be more widely known. The original archive, housed at the offices of Ordnance Survey in Southampton, covers most of England, Scotland and Wales and can be consulted by the public if advance notice is given.

Before their replacement by OS material in the second half of the nineteenth century, estate maps provide additional topographical information. They are particularly valuable in instances where the parliamentary enclosure map has not survived or where one was never made, agreement to enclose having been reached by the landowners and their tenants. They can also be examined in conjunction with the enclosure map itself, showing the situation before the allotment of land, though the area covered does depend upon the size of the estate in the area. Moreover, the maps help to fill in the internal field boundaries after enclosure.

Estate surveys, valuations and reports, with or without accompanying maps, give complementary material. Acreages are often shown and evidence can be obtained of the relative importance of open field and enclosed land. In this period they are more likely to mention the condition of the ground. A valuation of the Wolverhampton Grammar School estate at Rushock (Worcs.) in 1841 concluded that whilst the farms were on the whole 'in a fair state of condition and cultivation, the meadows and pastures had been neglected and needed draining'.[58] Beech Elm Farm was particularly run-down, being 'altogether in a very wretched state, it is naturally bad and is badly managed. The land wants thorough draining'. Such land benefited from the cheap loans which from 1846 the government offered to landowners to help them drain their estates. At Rushock, the work carried out under this scheme appears in the land agents' reports.[59]

Over the last hundred years the activities of the county councils, through their various agricultural committees, have had an impact upon the landscape. Perhaps most dramatically of all was the part they played in the wartime policy of converting wastes to farmland in order to increase the home production of food. In the First World War the Board of Agriculture set out to reclaim 4 million acres of rough grazing land and used as their agents the War Agricultural Executive Committees established in each county. Details of any improvements made under the scheme, together with much incidental information, can be found in the minute books of these committees. In Shropshire a survey of the different agricultural regions was made in 1917 and apart from the general descriptions of the areas, the acreages of agricultural and waste land were given (in round figures). The Wheatlands, potentially good arable land under proper management, was said largely to consist of poor grassland, much overgrown with thorns and briars.[60]

In peacetime other changes were carried through under the auspices of the various agricultural sub-committees and these can be followed in the pages of their minute books. The Allotments and Smallholdings Committee might authorize the taking in of wasteland for distribution among a number of smallholders or it might alter the field pattern to accommodate a large number of cultivators. Houses and outbuildings might have to be erected too. The work of the Afforestation Committee had an even greater impact upon the landscape. Similarly, operations initiated by the Drainage Committee had an effect, complementing the improvements made by private boards established by act of parliament. In Shropshire, a Drainage Committee was set up in 1920. One of its first schemes was the improvement of Melverley Brook, a project which entailed cleaning out the brook, providing flood gates, laying larger pipes and stabilizing the sides and bottom of the watercourse.[61] Work continued under the successors of the committee and between 1963 and 1973 alone the Land Drainage Department reclaimed some 60,000 acres in the county.[62]

To assess the changes that have taken place in the landscape over the past two centuries or so, local historians are helped by an increase in the amount of literary evidence available for analysis. More people were able to travel because of the transport revolution, though this brought losses as well as gains. Travel may have speeded up but close observation of the countryside was difficult for people enclosed in stage-coaches or in railway carriages. Among the best accounts is the one written by William Cobbett who rode around England on horseback in the 1820s and whose book, *Rural Rides*, depicts the landscape at a time of rapid change.[63]

More specific are the works of the agricultural writers. Arthur Young's accounts are particularly useful. Because of his passion for enclosure and his dislike of open-field farmers (he called them Goths and Vandals),he included much topographic information in his books. In his *Annals of Agriculture* (1791) he noted in the St Neot's area of Huntingdonshire, 'a vast improvement by an enclosure which took place 16 years ago, which has made the country much more beautiful and has been a great benefit to the community'.[64] William Marshall also described the physical appearance of the areas he surveyed, noting soil and land use, commons, woodlands and hedgerows, as well as field systems and the progress of enclosure.[65] The *General Views of Agriculture* include topographical details, though the evidence is variable in quality. Field surveys were frequently undertaken but were often performed in a cursory way. On the other hand, material on enclosure is normally given, if in general terms, and areas of open-field farming are described, sometimes even if they had recently been replaced by a new system. Moreover, it is often possible to compare conditions in individual counties at the time of the reports with later descriptions included in the essays published in the nineteenth century in the *Journal of the Royal Agricultural Society of England*.

Local newspapers should be looked at, especially for evidence of enclosing activity. Meetings of interested parties were advertised there, as were other public notices relating to the procedure. As such newspapers become more truly local, their value increases. Developments in the area were reported, and the mobilization of opinion for or against change was often organized through the newspapers. Instances of direct opposition were also recorded. On 8 November 1809, for instance, the *Salopian Journal* reported a riot in Dudleston Heath when 'a large mob of women and several men', comprising cottagers living on the heath, tried to stop the workmen digging the drains there.[66]

Photographs, of course, add an extra dimension to the study of the landscape over the last hundred years. Obvious changes are easily spotted – drained ponds, lost fields and shrinking woodlands and hedgerows, for instance – but more subtle developments can be detected too. Old photographs of Bookham Common illustrate this point. Those taken at the beginning of the twentieth century reveal a closely regulated environment with cattle grazing on the waste, but, with the abandonment of the practice, the natural vegetation has once more encroached upon the land. Aerial photographs offer a different perspective on the landscape. Moreover, because of the size of the area they cover, a general impression of the area and of the physical features which make it up can be gained. To these images can be added the reminiscences of the old people who lived through the changes, saw them being carried out and whose comments introduce a personal note to the events that took place.

Summary

Many documents provide evidence of the topographic changes that have taken place over the centuries and local historians should use them to reconstruct earlier landscapes of the area. Recent developments can readily be examined by looking at the material to be found on OS maps, in estate records and in tithe and enclosure awards. For earlier periods there may not be such obvious sources but much still can be done. As a guide, B. Harrison's article, 'Researching the Medieval Landscape', should be consulted.[67]

To begin with, the reader should prepare a base map upon which information gathered from such records as estate maps and surveys, deeds, manor court rolls, rentals and accounts can be entered. The tithe map is ideal for this purpose, although, if one does not exist for the area being studied, the first edition of the 6-inch OS map will do. As tithe maps tend to be large and cumbersome, they can be brought down to a manageable scale by either reducing a tracing or copy of the original (or blowing up a negative of it) or modifying the relevant section of the first edition of the 6-inch OS map. Once done, field – and other names can be put on it, beginning with the present day and then working backwards. Because of the descriptive nature of many of these names, a good run of early modern and medieval deeds might make it possible to discern various topographical features of the time, even if there are no maps and surveys (though these would be a help!). By carrying out this exercise local historians will be setting those agricultural developments that occurred into their proper context. There is a close relationship between the landscape and agriculture and an understanding of the improvements that took place in the one is essential if one is to make sense of advances that were made in the other.

Chapter Five

THE MARKETING OF AGRICULTURAL PRODUCTS

For farmers, the marketing of their produce was a matter of great importance. Very few of them were completely divorced from the business of buying and selling for even smallscale farmers needed money to pay their rent and to obtain the various goods and services they could not produce or provide from within the household. Nonetheless, specialist marketing institutions developed at an early date. In this country some centres may have had a continuous history of commercial activity stretching at least as far back as the Roman period, and others came into existence in Anglo-Saxon times.[1] Many more were established in the two centuries after the Norman Conquest, a natural response to the growth in the population that occurred.[2] This period marks the high-water mark of markets and fairs as trading institutions not only in terms of the number of centres but also in the relative amount of business being conducted there. The demographic crisis of the fourteenth century caused many markets and fairs to close, and, although there was a revival in the sixteenth and seventeenth centuries as population rose once more, the number of centres never regained the medieval peak.[3] Markets and fairs, moreover, increasingly had to meet the competition of other methods of doing business. The wholesale trade was the earliest to be affected, but the retail market suffered too. In addition, the traditional markets and fairs, came under increasing pressure from alternative forms of commercial activity.[4]

The establishment and distribution of markets and fairs

The earliest marketing centres owed their position to prescriptive right, that is, they based their claim on ancient custom rather than on specific grant. As a result, we do not know when many of them were founded. There are 58 market centres recorded in the Domesday Book but this is certainly an under-estimation.[5] No mention of markets is made in 14 counties, whilst one or two known to have existed at the time are not included in the list. The short-comings in the documentary evidence make other sources of information such as coins and place-names all the more valuable. The presence of a mint implies a trading centre, whilst the Anglo-Saxon place-name element 'ceping' means market. This suggests that places like Chipping (Lancs.), not recorded as market centres in the Domesday survey, were in fact acting in this capacity.

For some time after the Conquest informal arrangements persisted. Gradually, however, the Crown acquired controls over the establishment of markets and fairs, a development which culminated in the *quo warranto* procedings instigated in 1274 to determine by what authority existing marts were held.[6] Consequently, the process becomes better documented. The Crown, for instance, actively began to exploit its newly won authority, issuing charters to lords who petitioned for a grant (if the monarch acceded to the request and if a fee were paid) and disallowing markets which had not been so validated. Only those founded 'time out of mind', a legal definition meaning the period before 1189, were exempt. As a result of royal action hundreds of grants were made, establishing new markets and fairs or confirming others already in existence.

A record of the grant, if made after 1199 (when the charter Rolls begin), should be found among the Charter Rolls or perhaps in the Close Rolls. Many market grants were included in general charters of incorporation or in some other royal gift. Specific grants were given too, especially for additional markets and fairs. Confirmations of previous grants are entered onto the Charter, Patent and *Cartae Antiquae* Rolls and, for the period 1453–1625, the Confirmation Rolls. When new grants were made, enquiries (inquisitions *ad quod damnum*) were conducted to see if they interfered with neighbouring markets and fairs. This source provides additional information on the pattern of commercial activity in the Middle Ages and in the early modern period.[7] Inevitably, there are omissions in these records, and sources such as monastic cartularies and manorial accounts should be consulted for other references to markets and fairs.

The rapid rise in the population in the twelfth and thirteenth centuries, by increasing demand for agricultural produce, created the conditions which promoted the growth of a number of market centres. This development formed a part of the general pattern of urban growth, though, admittedly, a number of markets and fairs were situated outside towns. The main impetus behind the improvement in marketing facilities was given by the large landowners (including the Crown), who saw a means of obtaining a profit out of providing an increasingly valuable service. Naturally, the situation varied across the country. The greatest density occurred in heavily populated areas as new centres were created to cater for a growing local demand for goods and services. Markets were more widely spaced in areas of sparse population, and coverage appears to have been thinnest in upland districts.

Not all of the foundations were of equal importance; some were very small-scale affairs, short lived and ineffectual. Often founded later than those market centres which survived, they were generally established on less favourable sites and were among the first to go in the depressed conditions of the late Middle Ages.[8] Many villages today are failed medieval market centres, and local historians should be aware of this possibility. Topographical evidence may survive in the shape and alignment of the streets, the existence of a market square (now perhaps a village green) or even a market cross. Hallaton (Leics.) has both features. It may also be fossilized in street- or field-names like Cheapside or Fairfield.

When lists of markets and fairs were compiled in Tudor and Stuart times the numbers were much reduced.[9] Even if trade expanded with the renewed growth of the population in the late sixteenth and early seventeenth centuries, the commercial revival did not bring about the restoration of all the medieval markets. Some were revived and new ones were created, but the pattern of activity had changed. Rationalization of the system led to the establishment of a hierarchy of centres, and, whilst the more important ones throve, the smaller marts tended to decline and dwindle into insignificance.

Lists of markets and fairs can be constructed from a range of sources. Justices of the peace, who were largely responsible for overseeing economic activity in their counties, might occasionally record the market towns there: one account exists for Essex for 1575.[10] Almanacs and travellers' guides give more detailed coverage, noting the dates upon which the markets and fairs were held, as well as providing other useful pieces of information. Some are more comprehensive than others, but a selection of books should net most of the centres. Regular publications like Rider's *British Merlin*, which came out annually in the post-Restoration period, are of particular value. John Adam's *Index Villarum* of 1690 is another useful source.[11] Many markets and fairs are recorded in the topographical writing of the time, although the number will vary according to the area covered and the interests of the author. These accounts may include interesting comments on individual marts. Other references can be found in estate and farm accounts and in the depositions of witnesses in suits heard at the assize, in the quarter sessions or in the equity courts. From the details given not only can the number of markets and fairs in a particular area be worked out but also fluctuations over time can be discerned, as well as the contrasting experience of individual markets.

Just as marketing centres were not evenly spread around the country, so the times of the year when fairs were held varied. An analysis of William Owen's *Book of Fairs* shows a marked seasonal pattern with a major peak of activity in late Spring and a lesser one around Michaelmas.[12] This pattern was a natural one, reflecting the annual rhythm of livestock husbandry, the mainstay of business conducted at fairs. Moreover, when individual centres are examined in detail it is clear that spring and autumn meetings tended to do most business.

The conduct of business at markets and fairs

Most market centres acquired both markets and fairs, but occasionally only one or the other was obtained. Both institutions sold a wide range of goods but they differ in one or two important respects. Markets were held weekly and were principally used for the sale of corn and small produce. Fairs, on the other hand, had an annual cycle and dealt, to a greater extent, with livestock. Even if, over time, towns acquired additional grants, the basic pattern was not altered. In the North, however, the distinction was somewhat blurred by the existence of fortnightly livestock markets which performed the same function carried out elsewhere by the annual fairs. At Rosely Hill (Cumb.) they were held every two weeks from Whit Monday to Michaelmas and, according to Owen's *Book of Fairs*, specialized in horses, cattle and yarn. Surviving seventeenth-century toll books for Carlisle's livestock marts reveal a similar pattern but also indicate that one or two of the gatherings were far more important than the others and thus approximated more closely to the normal fair.[13]

Markets, with their weekly cycle and typical pattern of small-scale transactions based on the retailing of basic provisions, tended to draw their custom from a more confined area than did fairs. Catchment areas would often overlap, however, especially in areas liberally covered with market centres where farmers would have had a choice of outlets for their produce. Local historians could make a survey of the options open to farmers at various dates by drawing on a map a radius several miles in extent around it (Palliser and Pinnock used a 10.6 km radius for their study of medieval markets in Staffordshire)[14] and counting the number of markets encompassed within it. This could then be related to such variables as terrain, type of farming and landownership. Fairs catered for a longer-distance traffic. Livestock were brought to fairs on the hoof and thus could be moved over considerable distances.

Small farmers and the poorer elements of rural society no doubt had to make do with neighbouring markets and fairs but gentry and the more prosperous farmers had a greater choice. The size and quality of the market was a factor and one that became increasingly important as internal trade became concentrated on fewer outlets. Travellers' accounts, guides and directories often commented upon these differences. In Shropshire, for instance, Richard Blome noted in 1673 that Oswestry's Monday market was 'well resorted unto, and furnished with cattle and provisions', whilst at Ellesmere there was 'a mean Market on Tuesday'.[15] Similar judgements were made on the periodic fairs. The type of goods sold at individual centres was another factor. In spite of the wide range of commodities on display at markets and fairs, there was scope for specialization. In the 1720s Defoe wrote that Northampton was 'counted the centre of all the horse markets and horse fairs in England'.[16] At a number of places there were variations in the goods sold on different market and fair days.

Because of the records they have left it is easier to learn of the transactions made by the upper classes than it is for other sections of society. Medieval manorial accounts, for instance, reveal a considerable amount of commercial activity, often in the form of large-scale dealing in corn and livestock. The rolls may indicate the markets and fairs visited, though in this respect the source is a rather disappointing one. When one considers the amount of business being conducted, very few places are mentioned. A clue to the origin or destination of goods might be found in the section on miscellaneous expenditure, where the charges incurred by servants buying and selling stock might be recorded.

Later estate accounts are more likely to give the names of markets and fairs used. The reader should first of all take care to note the places included in the records; separate accounts were often drawn up for blocks of property on the estate but undifferentiated lists were also made and these might give a confusing picture of the flow of trade. Large landowners might move stock and agricultural produce around their estate and this could make intelligible their farming activities as well as their purchases at individual marts. The upper classes also tended to be involved in long distance trade in general. In particular, they were willing to send their agents far afield to obtain suitable stock. Commonplace books and estate correspondence fill in the details, providing evidence of the thinking that lay behind market decisions. Farmers' accounts and diaries are far less common but, where they can be found, contain the same sort of material.

Particularly valuable sources of information on marketing are the toll books which record the ebb and flow of traffic through a trading centre. Tolls had long been a major source of revenue to town authorities. These dues originated in the Middle Ages and consisted of a small charge on goods coming into the town – so much on every packhorse, waggon load or head of livestock. Evidence for the payment of tolls is not hard to find in corporation records (or in manorial records if the town was controlled by the lord of the manor). Unfortunately, the references are often brief notes indicating the sum collected during the year or the rent paid by the person leasing them. They are far more useful if the details of the goods being tolled are given. Early examples can be found, but key developments occurred in the second half of the sixteenth century when records of tolls had to be kept by law. In order to control horse stealing an act of 1555 ordered that all transactions were to be recorded by a specifically appointed tollgatherer who had to 'write or cause to be written in a Booke to bee kept for that purpose, the names, surnames and dwelling places of all the said parties, and the colour, with one speciall marke at the least of every suche Horse Mare Gelding or Colte'. A further act of 1589 tightened up the regulations;

henceforth all sellers had to be personally known to the tollgatherer or had to find 'one sufficient and credible person' who would vouch for his honesty.[17]

The trade in horses is therefore much better documented than other commodities but references to cattle, sheep and pigs and to goods like wool and leather can also be found. Taunton's toll books, for instance, regularly record sales of cattle and leather (and occasionally sheep), as well as transactions involving horses (see Appendix 8). Many sets of toll books have been lost and those that have survived decline in comprehensiveness in the late seventeenth century as private marketing grew. Nonetheless, there is sufficient coverage from different parts of the country for general conclusions to be made.[18] The toll books make it possible to look at catchment areas of fairs, fluctuations in marketing activity throughout the course of the year, the prices of animals (and occasionally other goods) and the classes of people involved. In particular, the books provide references to thousands of ordinary people living in hundreds of parishes around the country. Although only a small number of books have survived, many local historians will find evidence of the activities of members of their communities. Thus, most Shropshire parishes (and many in the neighbouring counties too) are represented in the Shrewsbury horse and cattle toll books of the late sixteenth and seventeenth centuries.[19] Moreover, even if the frequency does tend to decline with distance, concentrations of dealers existed which blur this general pattern.

It is interesting to note that whilst a few market toll books remain, they rarely record sales of grain and therefore do not adequately reflect the business being conducted there. Some books, like those at Shrewsbury in the late sixteenth century, list buyers and sellers of cattle, sheep and pigs as well as those dealing in horses and thereby indicate the catchment area of the market. At Chester and Oxford, on the other hand, only horses are entered in the books and they represent casual sales made by people visiting the city for other purposes.[20] They do, nonetheless, include references to many people living in the locality and their occupations.

Other sources require researchers to have an even greater amount of luck if they are to find material for their own communities. Quarter Sessions' and assizes' depositions, notably the ones dealing with instances of theft, might throw light on marketing patterns and organization. Some collections have been printed, others have been indexed or bound in volumes but many exist only in their original rolls. Similar material appears in the records of the equity courts at Westminster, especially those of the Court of Requests, but also in the Courts of Chancery and Exchequer. Typically, cases concerned disputed market rights, refusal to pay all or part of the purchase price of a commodity or non-delivery or misrepresentation of goods. These too are difficult to use. There are indexes but a great effort is needed to wade through them, looking for specific places or recognizable local names. State Papers are much easier to handle; with their place and personal name index and synopses of the documents to guide the researcher, relevant original material is more readily available.

Details of credit arrangements provide another source of information, especially in the early modern period when they were being used by an increasing number of people. Deals were often concluded upon the payment of a token sum of money, the earnest, with the balance being paid in regular instalments or at some agreed date in the future. Important dates such as Lady Day and Michaelmas were often used, as were the days upon which local fairs were held. Because of the obvious danger of purchasers refusing to pay up (and many cases of this appear in the records of the Equity courts), the practice grew up of asking them to sign a bond, enforceable at law to ensure payment.

Lists of credits and debts are recorded in probate wills and inventories and these can be used in a number of ways. Entries referring to places where the deceased's debtors lived could indicate the markets where farmers sold their goods. Similarly, tradesmen like butchers and bakers who processed agricultural products, might leave behind debts to farmers, thereby revealing their sources of supply. Unfortunately, the amount of detail given varies from document to document and as a source they do become less informative over time. In the sixteenth century individual debts are frequently specified but by the late seventeenth century they are often merely recorded in a generalized form. Moreover, even at an early date there may be only a single general entry in the inventory as the deceased had already written out the details in his or her will. Both documents might therefore be needed to obtain an accurate picture.

Regulation of markets and fairs

Open markets and fairs were subject to control by the authorities; numerous regulations were made over the course of time, and various bodies were involved in seeing that they were observed. Thus, information can be found in a number of different classes of record. Apart from relevant statutes enacted by Parliament, the privy council sent out a stream of instructions to local officials. For the years 1542–1631 the registers have been published in a series of volumes entitled the *Acts of the Privy Council of England*. In the counties the main agents of the government were the justices of the peace, and their actions and deliberations are enrolled in the records of the quarter sessions. At the local level, material should be filed with other manorial or borough records, depending upon whether a particular market was a seigneurial or corporate one. If special regulatory courts, known as piepowder courts, had been included in the market grant, evidence should be sought among their records. These local bodies dealt with many aspects of marketing activity – electing officials, collecting tolls, checking weights and measures, maintaining the quality of goods sold, correcting abuses and determining disputes. Whilst these authorities continued to run markets and fairs throughout the course of the early modern period (though piepowder courts suffered a decline), the business of enforcement increasingly was handed over to the magistrates working through the quarter sessions.

Basically the regulations sought to control the market in the interests of the consumer, especially the poorer sections of society, and to this end the measurements were designed to ensure that goods passed through the open market or fair and at a fair price too. This concern is shown in a proclamation made at the court leet in Guildford on 18 January 1528/9 which emphasized the need to provision the market with wholesome victuals and beer and condemned such abuses as forestalling and regrating.[21] For a long time the authorities were concerned about the activities of middlemen whom they felt were responsible for raising prices because they intruded themselves between producers and consumers. In particular, it was thought that such people were guilty of the illegal practices of forestalling, engrossing and regrating, activities which interfered with the flow of goods to markets and fairs and which offered the offenders opportunities for profiteering.

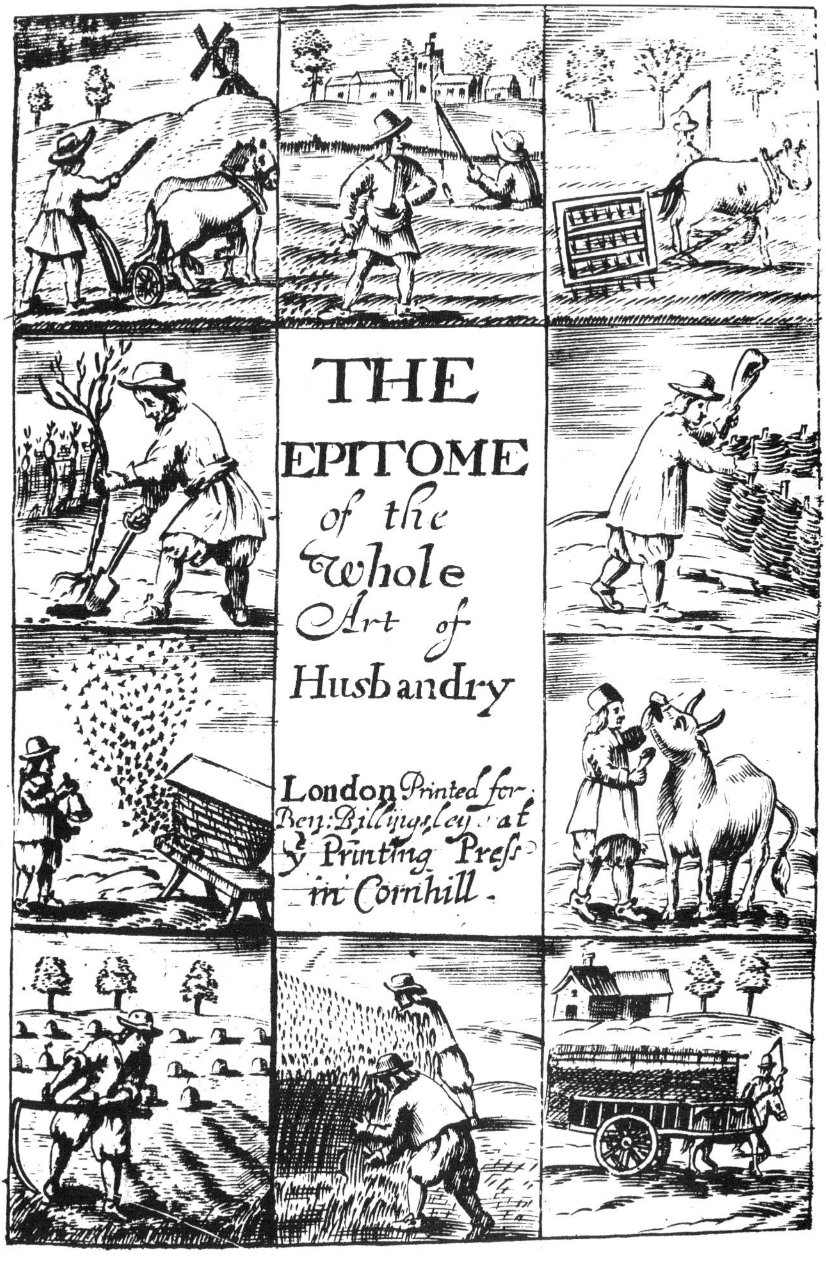
THE
EPITOME
of the
Whole
Art of
Husbandry
London Printed for
Ben: Billingsley at
ye Printing Press
in Cornhill

1 The frontispiece from
The Epitomie of the Whole Art of Husbandry by Joseph Blagrave, 1669

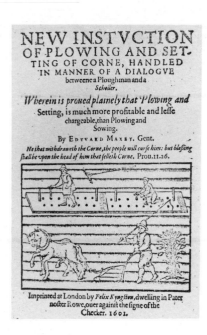

NEW INSTVCTION
OF PLOWING AND SET-
TING OF CORNE, HANDLED
IN MANNER OF A DIALOGVE
betweene a Ploughman and a
Scholler.

VVherein is proued plainely that Plowing and
Setting, is much more profitable and lesse
chargeable, than Plowing and
Sowing.

By EDVVARD MAXEY. Gent.

*He that withdraweth the Corne, the people will curse him: but blessing
shall be vpon the head of him that selleth Corne.* Prou.11.26.

Imprinted at London by *Felix Kyngston*, dwelling in Pater
noster Rowe, ouer againſt the ſigne of the
Checker. 1601.

2 *(Left)* The frontispiece from *New Instruction
of Plowing and Setting* by Edward Maxey, 1601

4 *(Above right)* Map of the piecemeal
enclosure at Church Aston, Shropshire, 1681

5 *(Below right)* Map of meadow ground at
Longford, Shropshire, 1682

3 *(Below)* Detail taken from a map of the township of Twyford, Shropshire, 1797

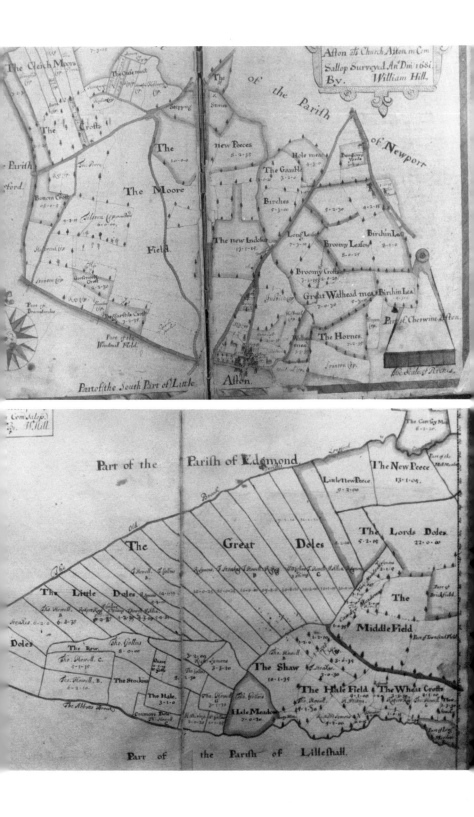

Aston als Church Aston in Com Sallop Surveyed An Dni 1681 By William Hill.

The Cleich Moore

The Ouse road

Slepping

The Crofts

Bottom Crofts

The Moore

Field

Part of Brownderhes

Part of the Windmill Field.

new Peeces

Hole mea

The Gamble

Birches

Long Leafon

Broony Leafon

Birchin Lea

Broony Crofts

Great Walhead mea

Birchin Lea

Part of Cheswine Aston

The Hornes

The Parish of Newport

Part of the South Part of Little Aston.

The Scale of Perches

Com Salop By W Hill

Part of the   Parish of Edmond

The Causey mea

Little New Peece

The New Peece

The Lords Doles

The   Great   Doles

The   Little   Doles

The Middle Field

Doles

The Row

The Stocking

The Shaw

The Hale Field   The Wheat Crofts

The Hale

The Abbots Brook

Hale Meadow

Part   of   the   Parish   of   Lilleshall.

6 Mixed farming: a reaper-binder cutting winter oats at Water Place Farm near Ware, Hertfordshire

7 A plough team at Troutbeck in the Lake District, 1940

8 A tractor engine pulling a plough
on a Berkshire farm

9 Cutting the hay on a farm near Wincanton, Somerset, *c.* 1900

10 Male and female farm labourers reaping and binding corn
on a Staffordshire farm

11 The arduous task of threshing

12 *(Top)* Men and women bringing in the harvest in the Henley-on-Thames area

13 *(Bottom)* Hop picking at Cranbrook, Kent, *c.* 1900

14 *(Top)* Children carting off the corn on a Sussex farm

15 *(Bottom)* The old livestock market in North Street, Guildford, pre-1895

In spite of the number of cases which can be found in the records, the authorities did not enforce the regulations with unremitting vigour. In practice, their actions tended to be crisis-sensitive. At times of plenty they tended to be lax in their vigilance but tightened up control when dearth threatened. On such occasions the government through the Book of Orders, first issued in 1587, called on the magistrates to carry out a number of measures in order to alleviate distress and to prevent profiteering.[22] The justices, therefore, had to look for corn stocks in the hands of people like farmers, factors, maltsters and bakers who dealt in the commodity and force them to send their surpluses to market at prices low enough for the population at large to buy. In general, moreover, they were ordered to curtail private dealing, to see that the markets remained well-stocked and to stop the diversion of much needed bread corn to such industries as brewing and malting.

Apart from the market officers, borough officials and magistrates, others were involved in the detection of market offences. These people were known as common informers and they made their living out of denouncing individuals engaged in unlawful activities (or accepting bribes from them if they did not tell the authorities).[23] Trading abuses were the mainstay of their business. As Professor Beresford has observed, 'Economic offences were those most zealously pursued, so that the informations provide details of an immense number of transactions in manufacture and trade in the period when the informers were most active, from 1550 to 1624'.[24] Until they were barred from the Westminster courts in 1624, they pursued much of their business in the Exchequer court. They worked through the quarter sessions and the assizes too, especially after 1624.

Common informers were motivated solely by financial opportunism, but the authorities too had regard for the fiscal aspect of regulation. There were profits to be made from toll receipts and from fines imposed upon those who infringed the regulations. The revenue collected by the market officials was noted in manorial or borough accounts; if broken down into its component parts, the account should give an indication of the relative value of different aspects of marketing activity. It is, of course, essential to have a comprehensive list, one which covers all the various items. In many places tolls were leased out from time to time and although the level of rent should reflect the economic circumstances of the day, the researcher needs to know exactly what had been let. Not all of the income was profit: owners were responsible for the upkeep and maintenance of their markets and fairs and had to pay the wages of the officers involved.

The decline of the open market and fair

The organization of the market did not change at once and for some considerable time the traditional institutions continued to exist, albeit in increasingly unfavourable circumstances. Thus, although the number of fairs tended to decline from a high point in the late seventeenth century, lists show that many persisted through the nineteenth century and beyond. For the second half of the eighteenth century William Owen's *Book of Fairs* is a basic source, supplying information on the number and location of markets and fairs, together with the times they were held and the commodities in which they specialized. Owen claimed comprehensiveness for his accounts: 'All the Lists of Fairs are full of great Mistakes, and in nowise to be depended on, unless signed with the Hand-Writing of Wm Owen'.[25] He was right to point out errors in the works of others, but his book has omissions too. It is, nonetheless, the best guide we have.

Commercial directories, which begin in the late eighteenth century and which become more numerous and informative during the course of the nineteenth century, can also be used. Some are better than others and wherever possible directories published by reputable firms, those which carried out their own research and which updated the information regularly, should be examined. Most directories of this kind print in the introductory section of each place an account of marketing facilities available (if any). Typically, Slater's Directory of 1849 notes under Loughborough (Leics.) that the town possessed a Tuesday market and seven dated fairs for cattle, sheep, etc. Because there should be a series of directories giving the necessary information, any changes that occurred over time can be observed. Lists of market centres in a county at the turn of the eighteenth century might also appear in the *General Views of Agriculture*. In the late nineteenth century other lists can be found in the Parliamentary Sessions Papers.[26] Apart from such compilations, the existence of individual markets and fairs can be discovered in such sources as newspapers, borough and estate records, and assize and quarter sessions' depositions.

Markets and fairs were still regulated by the traditional bodies, and records of their administration are located in the same sources as before. Seigneurial jurisdiction tended to decline during the course of the eighteenth and nineteenth centuries, though in places like Sheffield it was still important until the end of the nineteenth century. (The importance of borough records, on the other hand, increased after the passing of an act in 1875 allowing corporations to purchase the market rights). Agreements were not always arrived at overnight, however. At Sheffield it was 1899 before the City Council was able to come to an agreement with the lord of the manor over the price to be paid for the rights there.[27] In the eighteenth century a number of towns established market committees, and their records – books, minutes and accounts – provide a more direct and accessible way of finding relevant information than is possible in the old undifferentiated borough minute books. An examination of the papers of the market committee at Oxford which begin in the 1770s and continue through the nineteenth century show that it closely regulated the city's covered market. As late as 1824 it was attempting to prevent forestalling, engrossing and regrating.[28] At Leicester and Coventry the toll committees performed the same function.[29]

The continuing trade in livestock at markets and fairs is reflected in the entries in the toll books. Even if the source becomes less valuable as recorded sales decline, some idea of the catchment areas of individual centres can still be gauged from the books. Annual returns of corn, instigated by an act of 1791, provide information on the trade in corn and grain.[30] Under its provisions, inspectors were appointed to visit market centres to ascertain the average prices paid by buyers of various grains. The original information was kept locally but the worked-out averages were sent to the Receiver of Corn Returns in London. They have now been deposited at the PRO at Kew and are filed under MAF 10. Similar material can be obtained from the records of the assize of bread. The assize, which was of medieval origin, was used as a means of controlling the price of bread. Data was taken from buyers of corn, and the assize normally fixed at the second highest price paid. The material occasionally appears in manorial, borough and quarter sessions' records or in special lists. Documentation is somewhat patchy, with bunching in years of hardship when the authorities acted in a more positive manner. Oxford has a good series, covering the years 1692–1700 and 1733–1836, when the system was abolished by statute.[31] The documents should contain the names of the corn buyers interviewed, though their homes are not always given.

Carrier services listed in nineteenth century directories provide another source of information on catchment areas of individual marts. Towns and villages from which carriers set out or through which they passed are recorded, together with the days of the week on which they operated. Heavy concentrations of services going to market towns on market days suggest the importance of the market in attracting custom.[32] At Banbury (Oxon.) at the turn of the eighteenth century directories indicate a close correlation between the two, highlighting the town's role as a weekly market centre for villages within a ten-mile radius of it and for some others further afield.[33]

Newspapers should also be looked at for they not only chart the fortunes of the open markets and fairs at a critical time but also show the ways in which their primacy was being challenged. In particular, they reveal the ideas, attitudes and motives of the people involved – farmers, dealers, consumers and the authorities – in a period of change. Sometimes, a newspaper reported the revival of a market, as at Bampton (Oxon.) in 1766[34], or described a flourishing centre. More often, articles reveal a concern to preserve the traditional institutions in the face of attack from other methods of doing business. On 15 September 1753 an announcement was made in *Jackson's Oxford Journal* requesting all maltsters, bakers, innholders and others who dealt in corn at Oxford market to come to a meeting at the Mitre Inn 'to consider of proper methods to support our Corn Market, for the Good of the City in general'.[35] Topographical accounts, especially from the late seventeenth century onwards, also record the demise of a number of market centres. Town histories, which become more numerous and detailed in this period, confirm this trend.

Developments in marketing in the post-Restoration period

Developments occurred within both the traditional and the more informal methods of selling, though, as will be seen, they were often interlinked. The corn market was the first to be affected by the developments that took place. Corn was bulky and awkward to transport to market and as a result farmers in the late seventeenth century increasingly resorted to sample selling. Instead of carrying consignments of corn in wagons and carts, they merely took a small sample wrapped up in a pouch. At Oxford market sample selling steadily gained ground from the mid eighteenth century so that by 1795 a report in *Jackson's Oxford Journal* could state, 'Within the last ten years this practice of buying by sample has become universal'.[36] The advantage of such a system lay in its greater flexibility and convenience as well as in the saving that could be made in the payment of tolls. In March 1798 John Lamb of Sibford Ferris (Oxon.) noted in his farm accounts that he had attended Banbury market and had sold four quarters of oats to a Milcombe (Oxon.) man. The grain was delivered to Milcombe six days later.[37]

References to sample selling and to other means of disposing of agricultural produce also appear in county surveys such as the *General Views of Agriculture* and in those which formed the subject of essays printed in the *Journal of the Royal Agricultural Society of England*. According to Bailey and Culley, writing on the agriculture of Northumberland in 1805, Belford had a good corn market, 'great quantities of which are sold by sample'.[38] The Home Office papers should also be consulted, especially during the critical years of the Napoleonic Wars, when the authorities were particularly concerned about the provisioning of the market. The Privy Council papers contain other comments on the marketing developments in this period. Examples of sample selling can also be found in the papers and letters of the committee of the House of Lords appointed to enquire into the scarcity of provisions (1765) deposited at the House of Lords' Record Office.[39]

Farmers selling by sample could do so more privately, as they had no wares to set out in the market place. In consequence, much business was transacted elsewhere, especially in inns and other private premises, and, at inland ports like Oxford, on wharves.[40] Borough records are full of references to the attempts made by corporations to stamp out the practice, which made it more difficult to control trade and at the same time cost them money. At Devizes (Wilt.) in 1699 the Common Council noted that 'divers quantities and parcels of flesh, cheese, wool and woollen yarne' were being sold outside the open market, thereby defrauding the lessees of the market tolls of their revenue.[41] Though it mainly affected the sale of provisions, private marketing also had an impact on the livestock trade. At Shrewsbury in 1654 the toll book records the sale of 221 head of cattle, over four-fifths of which were disposed of at three suburban inns.[42]

'Farm gate' selling also became more commonplace. Farmers negotiated with dealers to sell their livestock whilst they were still grazing in the fields or their corn before it had been harvested. In the period before c. 1750 evidence of this practice can be found among the debts recorded in the wills and inventories of farmers. Late seventeenth century inventories of dairy farmers in north Shropshire reveal the business conducted with cheese factors who toured local farms for stock.[43] Estate accounts and correspondence provide evidence of similar arrangements on the demesne. In May 1686, for instance, Peter Booth, the steward of Paul Foley of Stoke Edith (Herefs.), wrote to his master to say that John Badham had bought the corn on the ground for £10 and had given a bill to pay it on 1 November.[44] Much later, in the late nineteenth century, the reports of the royal commissions on market rights and tolls provide further examples. At Taunton in 1888 Mr Baker, a butcher, deposed that he regularly used the fairs in the town but that, if he had the time, he would go to the farmers themselves. The reason for this, he averred, was the volatility of the market place which meant that he might get a better bargain with the farmers.[45]

Agricultural commodities were also sold by auction. Originally used mainly to deal with the sale of farm goods under special circumstances (normally upon the bankruptcy of a farmer or for want of a successor), the auction became a popular way of doing business in the nineteenth century, especially for the sale of livestock. Early examples of auctions turn up in farm and estate accounts from the late seventeenth century. When Thomas Aldwell of Slyfield Farm, Great Bookham (Surrey) went bankrupt in 1739 his goods were distrained and sold off at auction.[46] Interestingly, an inventory of his possessions was drawn up, allowing a comparison to be made between the prices noted there and those realized at the sale. Farm account books belonging to people who went to auctions as bidders reveal the operation of the system from the opposite point of view. An analysis of a number of accounts deposited in Reading University Library's farm records collection, for instance, makes it clear that some farmers regularly attended auctions to purchase stock and equipment.[47]

By the mid nineteenth century the work of auctioneers was beginning to have an effect upon the amount of business being conducted at markets and fairs. Many of them continued to use the traditional outlets but, as illustrated in surviving collections of auctioneers' records, they were increasingly doing business outside them. This trend can plainly be seen in the extensive archive of material (mainly accounts and correspondence) left by the firm Nock, Deighton of Bridgnorth (Shrops.) and which begins in the mid nineteenth century. Sales were made at nearby markets and fairs such as those at Albrighton, Bridgnorth and Much Wenlock, but most of the transactions seem to have taken place at inns. Sometimes it was the product of the year's farming that was being auctioned, on other occasions all the farm stock was being disposed of. In the accounts, information is given on the types and prices of goods sold, together with the names of buyers and often their residences.

Other sources can be used to examine the activities of auctioneers. They advertised in local newspapers, and entries should indicate the sort of items being sold. Estate and farm accounts, moreover, contain a record of the business that farmers did with them, though, as auctioneers are not normally listed as such, local records like directories, census returns and newspapers are needed to identify them. Diaries provide another source. Similarly, references to auctioneers appear in the reports of the royal commission on market rights and tolls. Some were asked to give their views, whilst other witnesses – farmers and traders, for instance – commented on their dealings with them.

Nowadays, we often think of the auctioneer in connection with the local Smithfield, essentially a livestock market site with pens and sheds, and normally located on the edge of town or near the railway. In general, the construction of such sites was a nineteenth-century development, undertaken to promote greater marketing efficiency and to free the centre of town from the animals. From the late eighteenth century covered markets and corn exchanges were also being built, another sign of the move from the open market place. Shops, moreover, grew in numbers to serve as alternative retail outlets. Necessary authorization for the building of new marketing facilities had to be obtained by statute, and local historians should look at the details written in the appropriate acts to see what was being undertaken. Newspapers reported the procedings and followed the course of construction. Such developments show that, in spite of the decline of the traditional institutions, urban population growth in the late eighteenth and nineteenth centuries necessitated some form of marketing structure to deal with the increased demands of a rising population. What emerged was not entirely new but merely an adaptation of some of the existing practices to meet changing circumstances.

In the twentieth century the development of farm co-operatives and marketing boards has meant further changes in the organization of the market. Farmers had long been urged to work together, but the impetus behind such schemes was given by the slump of the 1920s. Week after week the farming press was filled with reports of abuses of the market caused by the control which middlemen exercised over it and, as a result, it was recommended that farmers should co-operate in order to give them greater strength in their dealings.[49] The Agricultural Marketing Acts of 1931 and 1933 established a mechanism whereby producers of any agricultural or horticultural product could combine together to regulate the sale of that commodity. As a result, marketing boards for potatoes, hops, milk, pigs and bacon were set up.[50] Whilst the latter two schemes had folded by 1939, the other three boards throve, especially the Milk Marketing Board.[51] In 1957 the British Egg Marketing Board was established by Act of Parliament, requiring it to buy all the eggs offered to it but allowing farmers to sell directly to their customers if they could obtain a better price that way.[52] In addition, there is a British Sugar Corporation, a government rather than a farmer controlled body, which buys up all the sugar beet in the country.[53]

The involvement of farmers in such enterprises can be uncovered in their papers and accounts or can be ascertained by talking directly to them. The boards have their own records too, which provide information on the management of the business and their contacts with individual farmers. Newspapers also report such developments. In the *Sussex Express* in the 1920s and 1930s, for instance, information can be obtained on the progress of the two main co-operative societies which competed for the collection and marketing of farm produce in the county.[54]

Dealers, carriers and drovers

Because of the regulations which for centuries bound the actions of middlemen, evidence of their activities can be obtained from the records of bodies like the quarter sessions, and piepowder, borough and manorial courts which administered them. Similarly, the records of the equity courts, especially those of Requests, indicate in passing the way in which dealers carried on their business. Dealers acting lawfully can also be identified from these records. In 1552 they were allowed to operate under certain conditions; they had to be licensed by three magistrates but as long as they did not forestall the market or cause the price of corn to rise above a certain level, they could buy grain, cattle, fish, butter or cheese where they wished and resell it in the open market or transport it around the coast. In 1563 these measure were tightened up; dealers (listed as drovers, badgers and broggers) could be licensed only at a general quarter session and they had to be married householders at least 30 years' old. Moreover, they had to have been resident in the county for at least three years. Incidentally, the licensing laws for corn were relaxed in 1663, when unrestrained engrossing was allowed if corn prices fell below a certain level.[55] In 1772 they were repealed.

Lists of licensed dealers and presentments of unlicensed ones regularly appear in the records of the quarter sessions, even if their content is variable. At the Epiphany sessions in 1653 the Lancashire justices licensed 139 middlemen in Salford Hundred alone. In Kent, on the other hand, only 90 recorded licenses were granted in the years 1662–1706.[56] These licences normally indicate the goods in which each individual traded. In Shropshire the extant list covers the years 1613–1714 and records a number of cattle drovers and dealers in cheese, two of the county's agricultural specialities.[57]

For the livestock trades toll books are a particularly useful source for information on middlemen. Dealers may occasionally have been classed as such but more commonly were listed as chapmen, a general term given to dealers in any commodity. Even if they are not revealed by name, middlemen can readily be identified by the number of animals they bought or sold, by the frequency with which they appear in the lists and by their connexions with known dealers. An analysis of toll books of various Midlands fairs indicates that in the seventeenth century horse dealers were responsible for moving large numbers of animals across the country.[58]

The toll books reveal another significant feature of marketing in the early modern period, namely, the existence of family dynasties trading in certain commodities. Parish registers and probate wills help to fill in the family relationships. Probate wills (and inventories) also illustrate the way in which dealers developed their own social as well as economic networks. They intermarried, appraised colleagues' goods, and acted as executors, overseers and witnesses of each others' wills. When Richard Stockton of Bobberhill (Cheshire) died in 1583 the appraisers of his goods included John and Owen Griffith, whilst his sons-in-law, Randle Stoke and Owen Wickstead, acted as executors of his will. All five men were horse dealers.[59]

Probate inventories of dealers do not always reflect the scale of their activities, perhaps as they were unable to do business in their last illness. In particular, livestock are not well represented. Stock may have been disposed of by the time that the inventory was drawn up, either because the legatees and acquired them unofficially or because they had been sold to pay for the deceased's debts. The list of credits and debts, of course, may provide further evidence of their activities.

When provincial newspapers began to appear in the eighteenth century dealers were not slow to advertise their wares in them. In October 1751 a hop dealer from Market Harborough (Leics.) announced in the *Northampton Mercury* that he would be at the Woolpack Inn in Northampton for several market days where he would sell a large quantity of hops he had acquired 'as cheap as in London'. Other references to trading links turn up in newspapers. William Friend, a Deal maltster in the early eighteenth century, for instance, obtained seed oats and peas for Wales which he imported through the port of Sandwich. In the early Spring of 1730 he placed an advertisement in the *Kentish Post*, offering 100 quarters of black oats and 50 quarters of grey peas for sale.[60]

Any trading connections which dealers made with landowners and farmers should appear in farm and estate records and can easily be discovered if the people involved are identified as dealers. Where dealers are not classed as such, other sources may reveal their presence. In the early modern period toll books and quarter sessions' licences can be used. In the eighteenth and nineteenth centuries advertisements in newspapers should be searched for references to dealers, whilst in the latter century commercial directories and national censuses are also available.

When discussing the activities and status of one group of people who moved certain goods from one place to another, namely, the drovers, a distinction should be made between the men who made the deals and those who actually followed the drove. The term 'drover' was often used in the sense of a dealer, especially in sheep or cattle, and large-scale operators would have employed others to drive the animals. In an Exchequer case early in the seventeenth century two drovers, Thomas Johnson of Chester and Richard Higginson, a Shropshire man, took cattle, bought on the Welsh Border, down to the south-east. Johnson purchased the beasts locally but hired more humble men to drive the herds to the London area where the animals were sold by Higginson. One such man was Randle Bickerstaff of Malpas (Cheshire) who deposed that was a drover of theirs.[61] Some men, of course, combined the functions of dealer in and transporter of goods. The hoymen of Kent came into this category, for they not only bought in corn but also shipped it up to London. According to the *Kentish Post* of 27 August 1729 one of their number, Robert Sharewood of Faversham, sailed to London on alternative Fridays, returning home the following Thursday.[62]

Carriers with their wagons or packhorses moved a variety of goods, of both an agricultural and a non-agricultural nature. The carrier network expanded in the seventeenth century and continued to grow thereafter. The coming of the railways did have an impact upon their business, especially on the long-distance traffic, but many carriers continued to operate for a considerable time. After all, goods and people still had to be taken to and from the station. Developments in the carrier service can be analysed by studying the entries in the almanacs of the seventeenth century and the commercial directories of the period from the late eighteenth century onwards.

Summary

Over the centuries considerable change occurred in the

organization of the market, developments that were brought about by the different requirements of people at certain times as well as by improvements in marketing techniques and transport arrangements. A number of sources can be examined for evidence of this process, though the amount of information they yield varies. Thus, in the Middle Ages much is known of the expansion in the number of market centres from the records of central government. On the other hand, manorial accounts, whilst revealing the scale of marketing activity, are often vague about the people who were buying goods from the demesne or who were selling goods to the landlords. In the sixteenth century this deficiency is made up by the appearance of estate accounts which often do provide this material. In the early modern period, too, other sources emerge. For the livestock trades, especially that in horses, toll books are invaluable. The proliferation of provincial newspapers during the course of the eighteenth century offers a further source of evidence. At the end of the nineteenth century the royal commission on market rights and tolls give numerous insights into the way the marketing structure had changed and adapted to meet a different set of circumstances. A good deal of information on inland trade over the centuries can also be obtained from the records of the bodies that regulated the market – the quarter sessions, the borough and the manor. If, like the records of the equity courts, they often dealt with abuses of the system, they nonetheless help to fill in the details of the way in which the market was organized.

Part Two

TENURE, THE WORKFORCE AND TECHNOLOGY

Throughout history the possession of land has conferred status on the owner. Indeed, until comparatively recent times the power and influence wielded by an individual, both locally and nationally, was largely determined by the amount of land he held. At all levels freeholders enjoyed certain advantages denied to tenants, especially in the Middle Ages when the holding of land off another brought with it personal subordination as well as economic dependence. Even if the relationship was gradually transformed into a purely economic one, informal means of control persisted. In particular, in communities dominated by a single large landowner tenants had little freedom of action. In villages in divided ownership, on the other hand, social control was correspondingly less. This distinction between closed and open communities (with numerous gradations in between) is an important one because it not only reflected differences in social structure but also influenced the life of the inhabitants who lived there.

The distinction between free men and others has never been a clear-cut one. In the Middle Ages in particular there were degrees of freedom, and lawyers had difficulty in deciding which side of the line some people should be placed. Moreover, one has to distinguish between the personal status of the individual and the mode of tenure by which specific plots of land where held. Thus, in medieval times some freemen held servile land, whilst villeins obtained freehold property. It did lead to complications, however. Freemen could find themselves reduced to servility as a result of acquiring unfree land. Villeins, on the other hand, might be forced to surrender their purchase to the lord, receiving it back in bondage. In the late Middle Ages conditions eased as so much land became available in the aftermath of the demographic crisis of the fourteenth century. In the early modern period there was even greater overlap: as the danger of personal subjection receded with the ending of servile tenure, customary land became more sought after and many freeholders (amongst others) obtained it.

In the Middle Ages most people, including freeholders, held their land in return for certain dues their owed their lord. For many tenants this included the obligation to work on the demesne for part of the time. Bondmen had the greatest burdens. Those performed by freeholders were far lighter and had in any case been largely commuted to money payments at an early date. By the end of the Middle Ages the unfree tenantry had largely extricated themselves from these impositions too, though they did survive in an attenuated form in many places throughout the sixteenth and seventeenth centuries. Nonetheless, by then most of the work on farms not performed by members of the family was being carried out by hired labour.

Clearly, the workforce was not a static one; not only did its composition change over time but so did its size both in absolute terms and relative to the population as a whole. More labourers were needed in arable areas than in pastoral ones and at times the emphasis switched between the two. In particular, agricultural improvements could provide more work, increasing the demand for labour through more intensive methods of husbandry. On the other hand, enclosure, especially if it led to the conversion of arable land to pasture, reduced the number of job opportunities. Other technological developments occurred which raised farming efficiency. Apart from drainage and enclosure, they included improvements in hand tools, as well as advances in traction and power sources. Mechanization in the nineteenth century undoubtedly brought about a considerable saving in labour, but its adoption was not necessarily a negative and destructive event. In many cases machines were introduced only when labour became scarce and expensive, thus complementing the workforce rather than replacing it.

To help them in their work farmers and labourers had a range of tools and equipment which over the centuries were improved and developed. Farm buildings were modernized too. Advances in design and construction of buildings and implements helped agricultural become more efficient, even in the pre-modern age, and as a result output rose. The onset of mechanization further stimulated production, though its impact was not as sudden nor as dramatic as it might have been. Many farmers, as has been indicated above, were somewhat reluctant to use machinery, and its adoption therefore was often delayed for a considerable time. Changes also occurred in power sources. Traditionally, muscle power provided the main motive force and the speed and endurance of men and beasts regulated the amount of work that could be done in a day. Both horses and oxen were employed as draught animals and the debate over their respective merits continued for centuries, the outcome not being finally determined in favour of horses until the end of the nineteenth century. By that time steam power had been harnessed to farm machinery and this speeded up such operations as threshing and (to a lesser extent) ploughing. In a further advance the internal combustion engine has, in the present century, replaced earlier forms of power.

Chapter Six

TENURE

Freeholders

In theory all land in England after the Norman Conquest belonged to the king but in practice much of it had been granted to others in return for certain services. Thus, in 1086 William and the various members of the royal family personally controlled only 17 per cent of the land, according to the valuation in the Domesday Book. Apart from a miscellaneous group holding 8 per cent of the land, the rest had been given to 170 or so tenants-in-chief, a group of lay barons and ecclesiastical establishments who held directly of the crown in return for the provision of a set number of knights.[1] In turn, the tenants-in-chief settled the knights on the land, and these were the people with whom the ordinary villager was more likely to come into contact. This process of subinfeudation had already developed rapidly between 1066 and 1086.[2]

In origin these knights owed personal military service to their lord, but this simple arrangement did not last very long. Even before the end of the eleventh century such service was being commuted into a monetary payment known as scutage, and this trend became more pronounced over time. Moreover, as knights' fees fragmented and more rungs were added to the feudal ladder, it would, in any case, have been difficult to pinpoint the person whose responsibility it was to perform the service.[3] IPMs often highlight the complexities of the system with individuals standing in different relationships to a number of lords and tenants.[4] The Hundred Rolls of 1279, as well as manorial surveys and extents, provide other examples of people holding for fractions of a knight's fee or paying scutage.

People who held land by knight service were subject to other obligations. They owed their lord a relief, a sum of money, when they inherited their property and aids, payments made on special occasions. They owed him homage and fealty too and had to do suit at his courts. If they died, leaving an under-age heir, their lord had rights of wardship and marriage over them, a custom which could be turned to his advantage. As the Middle Ages wore on the rationale behind these feudal dues became less and less obvious and by the sixteenth century had ceased to have any meaning at all. People resented paying these archaic dues, especially those of wardship and marriage, which could not be only onerous but also open to abuse.[5]

Under Henry VII and his successors the dues were exacted with renewed vigour, and this increased people's hatred of them. Wherever possible, tenants concealed or ignored wardship rights. In response, the Crown established the Court of Wards and Liveries in 1540 to uphold its rights in this practice and to collect the revenues due to it. The records of the court have been deposited in the PRO, Chancery Lane, and include such items as duplicate IPMs, surveys of land in wardship, deeds and other estate records. A record of some of the disputes that occurred over rights of wardship can be found among the papers of equity courts such as those of Requests and Star Chamber. As a result of this opposition, knight service was obolished by an act of 1656, a measure which was confirmed in 1660 when Parliament passed a statute ending all feudal tenures.[6]

In the Middle Ages some freeholders held by a tenure known as serjeantry.[7] In essence, such people had been granted land or some other perquisite in return for performing some specialized service. This could be military; many serjeants were given the task of organizing contingents of soldiers in the feudal host or acted as standard bearers or esquires. They also carried out a wide range of other duties, many of a distinctly humble nature. In thirteenth-century Oxfordshire, according to the Book of Fees, several ushers, falconers and foresters held by this tenure, as well as a dispenser, a larderer, a preparer of herbs and a naperer. These people, who because of the varied jobs they did came from widely differing backgrounds, can be picked out in surveys and similar documents. As a class, however, they had virtually died out by the end of the Middle Ages.

Apart from churchmen, who held by frankalmoign, all other freeholders held by socage, a term devised by medieval lawyers to encompass a number of different forms of free tenure. The word can be seen in the term 'sokemen', the name of a class of pre-Conquest tenants who had received their land on particularly favourable terms. The Domesday Book shows that they lived mainly in the North and East, the region of the old Danelaw, and this reflects the freer form of society to be found there. In the survey the word 'sokeman' is often used interchangeably with the term 'free man', as the reference to 'a free man who was wholly a sokeman' indicates. There were differences, however, and much depended upon local custom. Some men were freer than others![8] Later sources such as manorial surveys and court rolls, for instance, reveal the existence of anomalous groups like villein sokemen. This class comprised tenants of ancient demesne (those manors which had been in royal hands in 1066) whose status, according to Edward Miller and John Hatcher, 'combined an unusual mixture of servile obligations and free privileges'.[9]

Those who held by socage tenure were not subject to wardship but had certain obligations to their lord. These duties, which differed between individuals according to status and local custom, were recorded in custumals and extents, where lists of free men appear alongside other manorial tenants. As a rule, they were among the first to have their services commuted but, even if they performed any tasks, they tended to be much lighter than those owed by bondmen. They paid a relief when succeeding to their property and an annual rent, but these were fixed and often nominal. Many were also exempt from the payment of a heriot, normally their best beast or good, when taking a property. Most commonly of all they owed suit of court but here too they were in a favoured position. On many manors they had to attend only once or twice a year, whereas unfree tenants often had to go every three or four weeks.[10] Numerous presentments in the manor court rolls for non-attendance show that even then they often did not bother to turn up (see Appendix 2). These burdens were hardly irksome but their status gave them considerable benefits too. The Domesday Survey, for instance, constantly stresses the more favourable position that free- and sokemen enjoyed. Freemen could dispose of their property as they wished, bequeathing their lands and goods or selling them without any interference from the lord. Moreover, they did not have to seek his permission to leave the manor. Above all, they enjoyed the protection of the royal courts.[11]

In the early modern period most free men continued to hold by socage tenure. Although not as grand a tenure as knight service, an increasing number of gentlemen held land in this way because it was not encumbered with the same feudal obligations. Moreover, those people who lived in villages where the manorial authority was in decline or had vanished, probably did not even have to fulfil their residual obligations. There, freeholders enjoyed a tenure very similar to the present day one. Of course, some owed greater dues than others. On a number of manors surveys and rentals show that heriots still had to be paid upon inheritance, whilst some lords claimed the right of relief upon alienation of a freehold property or the payment of a heriot on every separate holding (if the freeholder possessed more than one). Here were further grounds for conflict, and examples of such disputes similarly appear in estate collections and in the records of the equity courts.[12]

The transmission of freehold property

The build up of some freehold estates and the fragmentation of others was a continuous process, achieved not only by purchase and sale but also by grant and bequest. In the Middle Ages, for instance, a considerable amount was granted away as the Crown and the nobles rewarded their followers or as gifts were made to the Church. The first charters appeared in Anglo-Saxon times and continued to be made after the Conquest, though surviving ones are not always contemporaneous or genuine (see above, p. 68). From John's reign grants made by the Crown appear in the Charter or Patent Rolls (after 1516 solely in the latter).[13] The original documents are kept at the PRO in Chancery Lane, but printed calendars have been made of the medieval material and should be available locally in large reference libraries. For grants of land to the Church the reader should look in cartularies in which a record of the gifts was kept. Incidentally, it should be noted in passing that much land changed hands as a result of confiscation. The Domesday Book reveals the effect of the widest ranging measure of land apropriation of all, whilst the records of the Court of Augmentations deal with the disposal of the monastic lands at the dissolution.

There was an active land market in the Middle Ages too. For the large landowners evidence of their activities can readily be found in manorial collections, in the piles of surviving deeds or enrolled in cartularies. One class of documents comprised the feoffment or deed of gift, a written record confirming that the purchaser had obtained livery of seisin, that is, had ceremoniously received a piece of the property (some turf, for example), in front of witnesses.[14] Witnesses who attested such charters were invariably freemen, and local historians should keep a check on their names and the numbers involved. The final concord was also used, providing a legal record of the transaction. Fines are a particularly valuable source of information for the medieval period because with few exceptions they are the sole record of the conveyance.[15]

Smaller freeholders were also involved, and thousands of deeds deposited in local and national repositories record the transactions they made between one another. In this respect final concords are of interest because of their survival rate; even if the counterparts have disappeared, the 'foot' of the fine can be looked at in the PRO in Chancery Lane. Elsewhere, a record of such deals is more likely to be found if the properties concerned were later added to a large estate. At Wigston Magna (Leics.), for example, much is known about the activities of peasant freeholders because their land in 1521 formed part of the endowment of Wyggeston Hospital.[16]

In the early modern period, new forms of conveyancing were available as lawyers invented ways of making secret transactions. As soon as the Statute of Uses (1535) abolished the medieval system of uses, the device known as the bargain and sale was introduced, using the terms of the act itself to make covert sales.[17] This loop-hole was blocked later in the year by the Statute of Enrolments, which stipulated that bargains and sales had to be enrolled in the records of the courts, either at Westminster (normally on the Close Rolls which until 1903 were used as a registry for private deeds) or locally with the clerk of the peace for the county in which the property lay.[18] Local historians may therefore find useful material in the records of such bodies, providing evidence of property transfers in their own area.

During the course of the seventeenth and eighteenth centuries, moreover, another form of conveyancing, the lease and release, was developed as a quick, simple and *secret* means of transferring property. As such, it was widely used until its abolition by the Real Property Act of 1845.[19] The documents are easy to recognize because the two constituent parts, the lease and the release, are found together, the one being folded in the other. Even if separated, these documents can be distinguished from true leases by the use of the terms 'bargained and sold' and 'to the intent and purposes that . . .

may be in actual possession' and by the fact that the two parts were made on consecutive days. Of the other devices employed, the final concord remained a popular (if open) alternative until its abolition in 1834. To it should be added another form of fictitious action, the common recovery, which was introduced in the sixteenth century. The documents were similarly enrolled among the records of the Court of Common Pleas.[21]

The practice of mortgaging property also spread. At first glance mortgage deeds might look like conveyances or leases because similar formulae are used. The key section is the proviso, for there it is stated that if the sum of money borrowed (plus interest) was repaid on a certain day the transaction was made void. Even if the loan was not paid back, the mortgagee (the lender) could not acquire the property so long as the mortgagor (the borrower) kept up the interest payments. As a result, the mortgage became a secure way of raising capital without the danger of losing possession of the property, even if those deeply in debt might have to do so.[22]

Inheritance customs in a locality also had an effect upon the transference of property. Formally, the most common practice in England from after the Norman Conquest has been that of primogeniture, although partible inheritance was the custom in Kent and in various other parts of the country.[23] Borough English, the custom whereby the youngest son inherited was also widespread. In operation, this practice was similar to partible inheritance for testators seem to have provided for the older sons during their lifetime. For the particular system that was being used in a locality, custumals might include a note of the way in which freehold, as well as customary, property was bequeathed. What freeholders did in practice, however, was often different from the theoretical position. In areas where primogeniture was the custom, for instance, many of them sought to provide for all of their children. Court baron records, because they deal with the admission to property of all inhabitants of a manor, should indicate what arrangements freeholders were actually making. In the post-medieval period, moreover, probate wills, especially those in which the individual bequests are listed separately, provide further evidence of their actions.

Customary tenants

At the time that the Domesday Book was compiled there were a number of different classes of unfree tenant in the country.[24] Of those mentioned in the survey, villeins formed the largest group. As they had the biggest holdings, generally between a half and a full virgate in extent, they occupied an even larger percentage of the customary land. They were followed by bordars, cottars and coscets (32 per cent), who were small-holders farming at the most half-a-dozen acres. Many had virtually no land at all, and at this end the group merged with the landless *valetti*. At the base of society were the slaves, who formed nearly 10 per cent of the Domesday population. They consisted largely of unmarried men who lived on the demesne and worked for the lord full-time. The institution of slavery, however, was decaying by 1086 and their role was being taken over by the *bovarii*, unfree cottagers who worked full-time on the demesne.

Unfree tenants were burdened down with far more onerous duties than were the free men. Many of them had to work on the demesne on a weekly basis and there were additional services to be performed at busy times of the year. As the Middle Ages progressed, there was a trend towards the commutation of services, though there were checks and the pace of the change varied regionally and even between manors on the same estate. Details of tenants' obligations can be found in surveys, extents and custumals and the subject is fully dealt with in Chapter Seven. In general, the villeins, the tenants with the largest holdings, had the greatest obligations.

Unfree tenants suffered other impositions too. They were bound to the soil and could not leave the manor without their lord's consent. If they did, they had to pay an annual due known as a *chevage*. The lord's approval, moreover, was required if they wanted their sons to go to school or enter the church. Apart from rents, often modest in size, they paid tallage to the lord and gave him money whenever their daughters married (*merchet*) or were caught acting immorally (*leyrwite*). When they died, their successors owed a heriot to the lord and perhaps a mortuary (the second best beast or good) to the priest. Finally, as in the eyes of the law they were under the jurisdiction of their lord, they could not petition the royal courts for redress of grievances relating to their land or conditions of tenure. Such matters, therefore, are recorded in the manor court rolls, and items like the ones just referred to can be found there.[25]

Manor court rolls are a particularly valuable source of evidence because of the light they shed on the operation of the system of land holding on a manor. The records of the court baron, because they deal with admissions onto land (in both free and servile tenure), note the rents paid and other (and often more substantial) outgoings such as entry fines and heriots. Fines were higher than rents and could more readily be adjusted in accordance with fluctuations in price levels. They were therefore used by landowners to improve their income in times of inflation.

Because of the importance of status in determining a person's role in life, disputes concerning rank often came before the courts. Court rolls also record instances of manu-mission, whereby servile tenants bought or were granted their freedom. The relationship between a family and the land it held is another area which can be illuminated by an analysis of manor court rolls, especially if used in conjunction with custumals. Inheritance practices can be discerned as well as the rights of non-inheritors such as widows and younger brothers and sisters. Even where primogeniture was in force, other members of the family might be catered for with small plots of land. Provision was also made to transfer property to a more suitable member of the family when a tenant grew too old to work or if the heir was incapable of farming the holding.[26]

After the dramatic fall in the size of the population in the fourteenth century conditions for the unfree tenants gradually improved. By the end of the century there was so much unoccupied land that in order to find someone to farm it many lords were forced to make agreements with their tenants. The negotiations dealt with such matters as rent, services and other conditions of tenure and, when agreed upon, the terms were fixed and written down in custumals and on the court rolls. As a result, servile tenure had virtually disappeared by the opening of the sixteenth century, though it survived on some estates until after the act of 1660 which abolished all feudal tenures. Indeed, because of the dues and obligations that these *nativi* owed their lord, their presence was carefully recorded in surveys and on manor court rolls. Nonetheless, the bulk of the unfree tenants had become copyholders, holding their lands by copy of court roll, according to the customs of the manor.[27]

The copyholders themselves tended to share certain characteristics. Apart from holding by copy of court roll, they owed suit of court (often having to attend meetings which took place every three or four weeks) and gave heriots when entering onto the property. There were differences, however. The services and the obligations that they owed, for instance, varied between manors. Many had to use the lord's mill and oven, whilst in places labour services still had to be performed, though, on the whole, they were much lighter than they had been in the Middle Ages.[28] The duties owed and the rents paid on a certain manor can readily be discovered by examining surveys and custumals (see Appendix 2) or by analysing the entries in the court baron records.

Such records also enable local historians to chart the main division between groups of copyholders, between those who had copies for lives (and sometimes for years) and those who could inherit their property.[29] In the former system, at the end of the term, which was normally for three lives, the property reverted back to the lord to be re-granted out or kept in hand. Typically, the copyholder put forward his own name, together with those of his wife and heir, or two of his children. Heritable copyholds, on the other hand, were devised to the heir, according to the local custom of inheritance (see Appendix 2). Copyholders of inheritance were in a much more favourable position than were those who held for lives or years. In particular, entry fines were often fixed and at a modest rate too. Even if arbitrary, they could not be pitched so high that they prejudiced the right of the heir to succeed. They therefore had to be 'reasonable' (in practice, one or two years' improved rent). Such copyholders did have to pay a heriot of a best beast as well, although this may have been commuted to a money payment. They had greater freedom of action too, being able to sell or mortgage their property.[30] Both types of transactions can be found in the records of the court baron. Because of the strength of their position copyholders of inheritance regarded their tenure as good as a freehold and in some ways better. Indeed, when in the early seventeenth century the Earl of Arundel offered the copyholders on his Shropshire estate the opportunity of enfranchising their land, many of them refused.

On the northern border in Tudor times a form of border tenure known as tenant right prevailed.[32] Although similar to copyhold tenure in many respects, it possessed certain characteristics designed to meet the special circumstances of the area. Because of the need to maintain a fully manned and equipped militia, tenants were bound to do military service on horse or on foot as and when required by the wardens of the northern marches. Apart from this feature, which was an essential part of the system, the mode of tenure varied from place to place. If holdings were heritable, small fixed fines (gressoms) were all that were exacted and often none were due at all. Elsewhere, fines were arbitrary but set at a reasonable rate (perhaps at a sum equal to four or five years' rent), with additional payments being made every two, three or five years. When James I united the crowns in 1603 tenant right was no longer necessary, but its conversion to southern forms of tenure was not achieved without some difficulty (see below, pp. 124–5).

Copyhold disputes

Because of the financial implications, the local custom concerning copyhold tenure was a matter of considerable interest to lord and tenant alike. Clearly, lords benefited on manors where copyholds were held for lives at their will because the entry fines they charged could be adjusted to reflect the true value of the land. In contrast, copyholders sought to prove that their holdings were heritable. Here was room for disagreement, especially as the true situation was not always clear. In the North the ending of border tenure in 1603 caused much trouble. James I, pressed for money, declared that Crown tenants now held their lands at will and that, in return for being released from border service, had to pay extra in fines and rents. As other landowners soon followed his lead, it was not long before the border area was in an uproar.[33]

When disputes broke out, preliminary skirmishes occurred at meetings of the manor court as the steward attempted to take copyhold property in hand or charge arbitrary fines, and the tenants tried to resist such moves. Appeal was made to manorial custom set out in custumals, surveys or memoranda noted in the manor court rolls and made manifest by the manner in which copyhold property had hitherto been demised. To improve their case neither side was above tampering with the evidence. At Church Stretton (Shrops.) in the sixteenth century the lord of the manor, Sir Henry Thynne, and his steward not only prevented copyholders from examining the rolls but also inserted (in Latin) the words 'at the will of the lord' after the phrase 'according to the custom of the manor' in records of admission.[34] For their part, copyholders might sieze the rolls and make their own alterations, or at least change the wording in their own copies. Members of the manorial jury, set up to determine local custom, might also give evidence biased in their favour.

If the dispute persisted, the case might eventually be taken to the courts, perhaps to be heard at the common law, but more likely at one of the equity courts.[35] Copyholders had recourse to the royal courts because at common law they could bring a 'personal' action like trespass against their lord, if not a 'real' one. Moreover, as the conciliar courts were based upon equity and not precedent, different rules applied there. Among the records are a large number of cases relating to disputes over land formerly held by border tenure. Many seem to have been decided in favour of the tenants, indicating that judgements were not one-sided.[36] Elsewhere, copyholders had their share of success too. In 1670, for instance, the long-running dispute between the lords of the manor of Church Stretton and their copyholders, referred to above, was ended by a decree in Chancery which found in favour of the tenants.[37] Sometimes, such decrees dealt with fictitious suits, brought before Chancery to put the force of law behind a prior agreement made between the two parties.

The decline of copyhold tenure

During the course of the early modern period the amount of customary land fell dramatically. Copyhold land held for lives shrank as it was converted to leasehold, whilst copyholds of inheritance were enfranchised. Locally, the pace and scale of the change can be assessed by comparing two or more consecutive surveys or even by looking at a single one, if glossed. At Chippenham (Cambs.), where a survey of 1544 was carefully annotated in 1636, over 500 acres had been converted from copyhold to leasehold between 1560 and 1636.[38] Another pointer to the change is the decline of business being carried on at the court baron. At the same time the number of leases being sealed would have increased.

The process of enfranchisement continued in a piecemeal fashion until the final demise of copyhold tenure in the 1920s, with occasional bursts of increased activity in between. In some places it was carried out at the time of a parliamentary enclosure award, the lord of the manor receiving an extra allotment to compensate him for his loss of rights in those properties. At Scotter (Lincs.) in 1812, for instance, the award reveals that the Dean and Chapter of Peterborough obtained an allowance of 425 acres *in lieu* of their copyhold rights.[39]

The position at the turn of the eighteenth century can be assessed by examining the *General Views of Agriculture*. Differences in tenurial arrangements were one of the themes that the reporters were specifically asked to look for and thus local historians have a general, if brief, overview of the situation in their county at that time. In Lancashire John Holt (1795) reported that only a little copyhold remained. In Cumberland, on the other hand, J. Bailey and G. Culley (1805) noted that 'by far the greatest part of this county is held under lords of manors, by that species of vassalage called *customary tenure*'.[40]

Leaseholding

The Middle Ages

In the Middle Ages and for some time afterwards land that had been leased out was said to be 'at farm' and the lessee, the 'farmer'. Many lessees were also farmers in the modern sense, cultivating crops and raising animals on the land they had leased, but the term does not necessarily imply it. This distinction is an important one to make for on many manors the actual occupiers of the land were different from the people who had negotiated the lease with the owner. Unfortunately, sources of information like surveys and rentals often merely give the names of these tenants and do not show the extent of subletting that they engaged in. Much copyhold land was sublet too, and as a result, far more land in practice was held by lease than would appear from a cursory glance at the records.

Some of the largest leases were those in which manorial demesnes or even whole manors were farmed out. If the latter, the running of the manor court (and the profits derived from it) were invariably excluded from the lease.[41] For local historians this means that they still have manor court rolls to look at even if the manorial accounts are no longer very informative (see above, p. 24). On many manors the demesne was not leased out as an entity but was divided up into smaller parcels and let separately. During the thirteenth century, however, an increasing number of landowners took their land back in hand in order to benefit from the rapid rise in the price of farm produce.[42] When demand fell again in the fifteenth century, many of them reverted back to the old leasing system.

Apart from the demesne, other types of land were regularly farmed out. Assarted land, if not held freely by peasant colonists, was often leased. Because of the large-scale expansion onto the wastes in the twelfth and thirteenth centuries, leasehold land therefore increased considerably. . Rentals, surveys and extents, when recording assarts, often make the distinction between recent ones and those which had been in existence for some time.[43] Rents per acre tended to be higher on new intakes, reflecting the growing demand for land. Customary land might also be leased, especially in the later Middle Ages when, because of a shortage of tenants, the lord often had property in hand for a time. The same thing happened to freehold land, which came into a lord's possession because the heir was under age.

The Domesday Book contains a number of examples of manors which were out at farm. Many of the royal manors were, in fact, in lease in 1086. Where the latin word *reddit* (it renders) is written down instead of the term *valet* (it is worth) one can assume that the property was being farmed.[44] The survey also reveals that leaseholders came from widely differing social classes. The men who farmed the crown manors were often important local barons, but there were many others, leasing a small area of land, who came from a much more humble background.

One large group of rent payers in 1086 were known as *censarii*.[45] They were to be found almost exclusively on northern manors in Yorkshire, Derbyshire, Nottinghamshire and Lincolnshire, though people of similar standing undoubtedly existed elsewhere, if under another name. The conventionary tenants of Cornwall, for instance, could be either free or unfree but were essentially leaseholders.[46] They held their land on seven years' leases at rents which they could negotiate but had no automatic right of renewal whenever their term was up. Their labour services were light and rarely demanded, but if unfree, they were subject to the customary servile incidents.

All these variations can be seen in later medieval records.

When a survey of the Worcester Cathedral Priory estate was made in 1240–2 about one-quarter of the demesnes had been leased out. [47] Clearly, if part or all of the demesne were carved up into parcels, peasant farmers were more likely to obtain a lease than if it were let entire. The leaseholders might form a separate class, but surveys indicate that many of them also held free or customary land too. At Ardleigh (Herts.) in 1222 many of the leaseholders of demesne parcels were villeins, whilst the *censarii* were among those villagers who also held old assarted land, rented out at 4d. an acre. [48]

Details of individual leases (name of lessee, the fine, rent and term) should be found on the manor court rolls. Medieval leases were granted for a term of either years or lives. In the later Middle Ages the terms tended to lengthen as landowners tried to attract tenants onto their land. Some of the best evidence can be obtained from monastic cartularies and the entries there show that medieval leases could be quite sophisticated. [49] Leaseholders also appear in manorial accounts, where their rents are listed with other items of income. Rentals provide the same sort of information. Indeed, on a manor where the land had been largely or wholly farmed out, the annual rent roll would look remarkably like the rent collector's account. On the Durham Cathedral Priory estate (and elsewhere) they were used as such. [50]

Data obtained by looking at material relating to the principal leaseholders has to be modified by the knowledge that much of the land that they held was sublet to others. There were various motives for this practice. An important consideration was the changing needs of an individual over the course of his or her life. As a person's family expanded, extra land would be needed to feed the additional members. In later life this trend was reversed and a smaller holding would suffice, thereby freeing land for someone else. Perhaps John Payne and Alice, his wife, who sublet their land in Chobham (Surrey) in 1340–1 came into this category for at a court held that year the lord of the manor granted them a corrody (an allowance of food, beer and clothing) for life. [51] Many subtenancies, moreover, were created for dependent relatives – younger sons and brothers – providing them with some access to the land. Not all subtenants were poor people, however, for many enterprising peasants acquired land in this way. [52]

In the period before the early fourteenth century lessees

holding land on easy terms could capitalize on the growing demand for land by charging large rents for pieces of property. The subtenants, moreover, often laboured on the main tenant's holding and helped him fulfil his labour services on the demesne. At Meon (Hants.), for instance, when one tenant of the manor came to perform his harvest works, he arrived with 25 subtenants.[53]

An alternative arrangement was the system of share-cropping, referred to in medieval documents as leasing *at champart*. This was particularly useful for people who were growing too old to do the work themselves or, for one reason or another, needed someone to cultivate the land. Normally, a person would agree to take on the holding, carrying out the jobs of preparing the land, sowing and reaping the corn and tending the animals, in return for a half the produce.

Some indication of the incidence of subletting can be obtained from the licences granted by the lord and entered in the manor court rolls. However, because it was a widespread custom that subtenancies of two or three years did not have to be licensed, many went unrecorded. Here was scope for sharp practice. As a seventeenth-century surveyor of Orwell (Cambs.) was later to note of the tenants there, 'they pretend they may let estates by deeds for three years without licence'. As a result, 'they let leases for three years to three years *ad infinitum*'.[55] Occasionally, other references to the practice appear in the court rolls, notably whenever disputes arose between tenant and subtenant.

Subtenants are mentioned in some extents and surveys, and when this information is given local historians can assess more accurately the size of the holding actually being worked. At Havering (Essex) a survey taken in 1352/3 not only lists most of the subtenants of the main tenants but also notes their subtenants too.[56] There were 187 people who held directly of the king, but to this figure must be added 253 others known to hold land only as subtenants. The Hundred Rolls of 1279 and rentals are other sources which might provide useful information. At Kibworth Harcourt (Leics.) several rentals listing the subtenants of the manor were made at the end of the thirteenth century and in the early fourteenth century, which, even if they do not give acreages, do at least indicate the number of people who held land of each tenant.[57]

The post medieval period

As in the Middle Ages, leasehold property was being made out of demesne land and enclosures from the wastes. Additional leaseholds were formed from old owner-occupied land and copyholds for lives. In practice a considerable amount of the surviving copyhold land was also being leased out in the form of subtenancies. Small freeholders may have had to sell out to large landowners in times of distress but there does not seem to have been the same compelling reason for the conversion of copyholds at will to leasehold. The change, however, did bring manorial lords added benefits.[58] It gave them certainty of control over the property. Instead of having to depend upon possibly unreliable manorial juries to uphold their rights, they could enforce them through covenants incorporated into the lease. It also enabled them to regulate subletting to a greater extent and to eliminate the practice of the window's bench (the right of the window of a tenant to all or a part of the property for her life). The latter custom gave many copyholders an extra free life, but it was open to abuse.

In areas where copyholds for lives had been the norm, little change occurred.[59] Leaseholds, in general, were held for 99 years, determinable upon three lives, though, as before, the length of time and the number of years could vary. Similar provision was made for adding or exchanging a life, if the landlord wanted to keep the lease in being. By such means the tenant maintained his hold on the property, whilst the landlord acquired a regular source of income. At Kinnersley (Shrops.) a lease of 1729 allowed the tenant to exchange a life for £30 or to add one for £60.[60] The method of payment remained the same too, with high entry fines providing the bulk of the income. In addition, heriots were still demanded.

Whilst leases for lives were a characteristic feature of the West, in eastern England leases for years were more common.[61] In the early sixteenth century many long leases were made, continuing the pattern of the late Middle Ages. On the eve of the dissolution, much monastic land was let out in this way, as the monks sought to cash in before their property was appropriated. In the second half of the century surveys and individual leases show that the years shortened as demand for land grew; 7, 14 or 21 years were the usual terms referred to in leases, with renewal possible every 7 years. Here too, high entry fines were in general use as a means of paying rent well into the seventeenth century. By 1650, however, the charging of economic or rack rents (that is, a rent reflecting the true value of the property) had made considerable progress. In fact, as much sublet land was held on the rack, the practice was even more widespread than it might appear.

In the East annual tenancies made greater headway in the seventeenth century too. These took two forms: tenancies-at-will and leases from year to year.[62] The former method was one generally restricted to the letting of cottages, small-holdings, parcels of land and the like and as such was commonly regarded as an inferior form of tenure. The latter system, on the other hand, regulated by a formal agreement either verbal or written, had no stigma attached to it. In western England in the early modern period tenancies-at-will were largely used for the same purposes as they were in the East, but they also proved an effective ploy in bringing recalcitrant tenants to heel.

Over the country as a whole, the number of annual tenancies continued to grow, at a faster rate in the East than in the West, though the speed with which they were adopted varied according to the leasing policy of individual land-owners and to the attitude of their tenants. In the later eighteenth century, for instance, there was considerable debate about the respective merits of leases and annual tenancies,[63] which can be picked up on a county basis in the pages of the *General Views of Agriculture*. Arthur Young was one of those writers who favoured leases, believing that tenants would only invest money in making improvements if they had security of tenure. Landowners were divided on the issue. On individual estates the practices being carried out there can be discerned from sources such as surveys, leases and estate correspondence.

The issue was still a live one in the nineteenth century and varying views were heard by the Select Committee on Agricultural Customs which met in 1848.[64] By then, however, in general, opinion had swung towards annual tenancies, no doubt influenced by the problems caused by the wild fluctua-tions in prices and rents of the period of the Napoleonic Wars and the years immediately afterwards. Although surveys and leases show that on many estates property continued to be leased out, landowners and tenants alike were increasingly coming to appreciate the advantages which a more flexible form of tenure could bring.[65] From the tenant's point of view problems attendant upon a change of tenant were eased by the development of local customs to regulate the transitionary period.[66]

Just as for other forms of tenure, manorial and estate surveys provide the most obvious source of evidence on leaseholds. Moreover, the information they contain can be complemented by data drawn from individual leases which survive in greater numbers in the post-medieval period.[67] Tabulated by period, a collection of leases might reveal changes in policy on an estate. Leases, unlike surveys, were being made or topped up all the time, though the two sources might coincide if the former depended solely on the life of the landowner or were renegotiated *en bloc* at a revaluation of the whole estate. In general, therefore, leases had a different chronology to surveys and certainly provide a more sensitive indicator of change. They may also provide information on the people who were actually farming the land. When leases were being renewed or altered in some way (lives or years added or a reversionary interest granted), they often refer to the occupier as well as to the tenant, if different. There is a better chance of finding leases given to subtenants too.

In the post-medieval period the range of estate material increased as specialized documents were made for a specific purpose. At Kibworth Harcourt (Leics.) and, doubtlessly in many other places too, this was associated with the decline of the manor court as an administrative body.[68] A book of leases was begun around 1578 and in 1609 a memorandum on encroachments was made. Such documents are common, as are 'rentals' giving actual sums paid and an improvable figure. Their usefulness to the local historian depends, of course, on the proportion of land covered by the estate, though, as they might reflect normal practice in an area, they could have a more general value. A survey of leases on lord Kilmorrey's Shavington estate in the 1680s, for instance,[69] reveals the process of conversion of life leaseholds to leases for years at rack rents that was the being undertaken on a number of north Shropshire estates.

When analysing the information contained in such documents the problem of hidden subtenancies, encountered in medieval documents, must still be borne in mind, however. Dr Harrison emphasizes this point in an article in the *Agricultural History Review*, entitled 'Village Surveys: A Comment'.[70] As many subtenancies were for small pieces of ground demised for a few years, the situation changed rapidly. Even contemporaries were confused. At Whitchurch (Shrops.) the surveyor, who drew up the survey of rents for leaseholds and tenancies-at-will in 1598, admitted,

> Memo. in this last Rental delivered in by Mr Talbottes Offycers: There are sundry other Improvements & Increasinges both in leases and Tenements at wyll, which because of often chaunginges and are in new mens names and one man now hath asmutch as 3 or 4 had before yett are not in this Rentall distinguished Therfore they can not be examined or tryed by the Old Rentalls untyll further knowledge be had hereof especiallie because the Rent which one man payeth this yeare for hys Close, ys payde the next yere by other Tenauntes as every man hath used to hyre grownd.[71]

Some surveys, such as the Cannock survey of 1554 analysed by C. J. Harrison (see above), do indicate subtenants but they are no more common than they had been in the Middle Ages. Rentals too, as before, occasionally reveal the identity of the actual occupiers, as well as the names of the main tenants. Licences were still entered on the manor court rolls, whilst passing references to subtenants were often made in probate wills and in leases. One local historian, Peter Finch, has used a parish rate book to gain an impression of the size of this group, basing his analysis on the fact that such assessments were made on occupiers rather than on owners or main tenants.[72] Comparing a rating list of 1613 for the parish of Nutfield (Surrey) with admissions to property recorded in the court rolls, he discovered that subtenants greatly outnumbered tenants. There are problems to be encountered when using this technique, which are outlined in the article, but undoubtedly many local historians could employ it or adapt it according to the circumstances in their particular communities.

Insights into leasing policy on an estate can be obtained by looking at the correspondence between the land agent and his master. The conservatism of landowners can perhaps be summed up in the comment which John Bridgeman of Castle Bromwich (Warwicks.) made to his Shropshire agent, John Jones, in 1740. 'The reason why I am for a longer term of years than seven,' he wrote, 'is because I dont care to change now in my old age.'[73] Such letters cover a range of issues – the level of rents, the number of lives or years to be put in the grant, changes in policy, the respective merits of competing tenants, the problems of finding tenants and so on.

The unexpired portion of a lease could be bequeathed to someone else, and therefore wills should be looked at for evidence of a person's holding. Often the information is recorded only in general terms but some give details of leases. When Thomas Saunders, a Putney (Surrey) labourer, made his will in December 1614 he gve his son, Thomas, 'the ressidue of the tyme and terme of yerres to Coomme, thatt shall happen too be unexpired after my decease which I have & doe enioy by a lease which I did obtayne & gett of one John whittbrooke of Puttney in the County of Surrey Esquire'.[74] If the name of the landowner is given, as in this case, it could help the researcher by pointing him or her in the direction of the relevant estate collection. Leases, because they were classed as chattels, are also listed in inventories and thus additional information may be found there.

Inventories also reveal examples of share cropping, an arrangement which is easy to pick out because the appraisers list the fraction of the stock due to the deceased (normally, but not always, a half). In January 1707/8, for instance, Thomas Walworth, a joiner from Hopton in the Hole (Shrops.) left a half of 24 acres of corn at Downton ploughed and sown 'to half'.[75] When James Smith, a gentleman of Overton (Shrops.), died in 1667 his appraisers noted the name of the share cropper. James owned half of 4 acres of barley and 4 acres of peas which were 'between him and John Pearce'.

The *General Views of Agriculture* reveal wide variations in leasing practice in individual counties at the turn of the eighteenth century. In the North and West there were still many life leaseholders, though there is evidence to suggest that the system was in decline. In both Devon and Lancashire the late eighteenth century appears to have been the critical time. In Sussex, on the other hand, landowners either let their property for years, normally 7, 14 or 21, or granted annual tenancies.[76] Subsequent developments can be gauged by looking at the information printed in the articles on county farming which appeared in the *Journal of the Royal Agricultural Society of England* in the nineteenth century.

Summary

Local historians reading this account of developments in tenurial practices and the source that can be used to examine them may be a little wary of the medieval documents quoted. A good deal of space has been devoted to that period because many of the records used by early-modern (and even modern) historians were first drawn up then. Many of the themes remained the same too – the relationship between lord and tenant, the terms of the agreement and the means whereby land and other property was transferred from one person to another. The difficulties to be faced in obtaining an accurate picture of events, highlighted by the problem of subletting, are also similar. If the text tends to peter out somewhere in the mid eighteenth century it is because by that date the present day system had emerged in all its essentials. Moreover, very little can be added to the list of sources, other than to note that they tend to survive in larger quantities and to give greater detail. As an early-modern specialist, I would stress the importance of the time in the evolution of tenurial arrangements, but nonetheless there was a good deal of continuity from the Middle Ages. In addition, the amount of material which can be used to examine that period makes it a worthwhile and rewarding task too.

Chapter Seven

THE AGRICULTURAL WORKFORCE

The Middle Ages

Although many farmers in the Middle Ages predominantly used family labour, some did have outside help. Surveys of the Bishop of Worcester's estate, for instance, seem to suggest that yardlanders, and even half-yardlanders, might have had full-time servants.[1] Others elsewhere employed hired labourers too. Unfortunately, the evidence appears only intermittently and in an incidental way, and the best accounts of the medieval workforce are to be found in the records of demesne farming.

Manorial lords obtained their labourers from a number of sources.[2] Some of the work was done by unfree manorial tenants, the villeins, bordars and cottars, who paid a rent for their holdings but who also had the perform labour services on the demesne. In addition, there existed a class of tenants known as *bovarii*, who, in return for working full-time for the lord, were excused all rents and other services. Free tenants may have been involved too. However, many of them had commuted their labour services to a money payment at an early date and, even if they still performed them, they were comparatively light. The main body of permanent workers were the *famuli*, people who lived on the demesne and who were paid partly in wages and partly in kind. Casual workers were also used to carry out specific tasks or to augment the workforce whenever extra hands were needed. Many of them were labourers but some were skilled craftsmen like carpenters or blacksmiths whose services were needed from time to time. Of course, the emphasis given to each element in the workforce varied across the country, even between individual manors, and changes took place over time too.

Labour services

Surviving Anglo-Saxon wills and charters show that in many places farmers owed a range of services in return for their land. At Tidenham (Glos.) a custumal drawn up between 956 and

1065 reveals that, whereas the superior tenants, the *geneat*, carried out a number of unspecified tasks on and off the demesne, the lower status *gebur* worked there on a weekly basis, ploughing, reaping or mowing.[3] Weekly work continued to form the basis of tenants' services after the Conquest. In addition, at critical times of the year they performed extra boon works which might consist of ploughing, harrowing, threshing, haymaking or harvesting. They were also obliged to carry out carting and other specialized services. At harvest time, moreover, they often had to bring along their family to work with them.[4]

Details of the services that the tenants performed can be found in custumals, extents and surveys of particular estates and in the I.P.M.s that were drawn up after the death of tenants-in-chief. The dues owed by individuals varied, typically according to the amount of land held, but each class of tenant normally had identical obligations. To avoid repetition, therefore, it was common for specimen entries to be written out in full, reference thereafter being made to them where relevant.[5] Evidence of labour services can also be found in the Hundred Rolls of 1279. In some cases only terse statements were made but in others more information was given, providing the same sort of detail written in surveys and extents.[6] The Rolls, though they only cover a small part of the country, are therefore a valuable sources of evidence, not only because they augment the material obtainable from other records but also because they often deal with manors for which no other material exists.

In general, labour services were heaviest in eastern England and in Hertfordshire, Northamptonshire and Sussex. Here, two or more days' work a week was required, together with boon work at peak times of the year and other services. They were lightest in the North and the north Midlands and in the counties of Cornwall, Hereford and Kent.[7] The situation was a fluid one, however, and changes occurred over time. During the course of the twelfth century, for instance, many landlords allowed their tenants to commute their labour services into money payments. They did so partly because the growth of population made hired labour more readily available but also because the work they did was better. The tenants, nonetheless, remained liable to perform the services if called upon to do so, and as the demand for labour increased in the late twelfth century with the trend towards the direct farming of the demesne, the movement was put into reverse on a number of estates. It did not eliminate it, however, and thirteenth-century records provide evidence of the continuation of the practice. By the end of the century, commutation was once more in full swing.[8]

Clearly, even if there was an overall cycle of events, local historians will find that there was no common pattern between manors. Moreover, our knowledge of these developments is limited by the fact that most of the material is derived from the records of ecclesiastical estates and they may be atypical. Much depended upon local circumstances and varied according to such factors as the cost and supply of wage labour, the level of customary obligations and the type of husbandry being followed. Thus, on the cathedral of Worcester's estate heavy labour services persisted on a number of manors in south-east Worcestershire because of the long-established tradition of arable farming there. On some other cathedral manors commutation had progressed much further.[9] As a rule, weekly works were more likely to be sold than seasonal boon-works since it was often easier to employ wage-earners to do the jobs. In addition, there was not the same desparate need for labour as occurred at critical times of the year.[10] So that the lord would know how much to charge if he sold the labour services due to him, the works were valued individually and the information written down in an extent, survey or custumal.

Changes in the incidence of labour services may come to light when examining a series of surveys. At Minchinhampton (Glos.) three twelfth-century surveys exist and reveal that money rents were gradually adopted on the manor.[11] Surveys, however, were only made at irregular intervals and, as a static record, may refer to practices that had been in operation for some time. These deficiencies, which are inherent in the source, fortunately can be compensated for by an examination of the material contained in manorial accounts. Because they were drawn up annually to record items of income and expenditure, they indicate the actual situation on individual manors.

Hired labour

Work not done by the tenants was carried out by full-time employees, largely the *famuli*, or by casual workers. The permanent servants did all manner of work but in particular they were employed on regular farm jobs like ploughing, carting and tending to the livestock. At Kennett (Wilts.) in 1270 the accounts refer to 15 full-time workers, namely eight ploughmen, two shepherds, a carter, a cowman, a swineherd, a warrener and a dairymaid. This was a higher than average complement but the range of jobs is typical.[12] In addition to their wages, the *famuli* were given an allowance of corn, known as a livery, normally at the rate of one-quarter every ten weeks. The type of grain given varied from manor to manor, perhaps reflecting local preferences or practices.[13] Thus, at Downton (Wilts.) in 1324–5 only barley was provided, whilst at Petworth (Sussex) in 1347–8 more rye than barley was given.[13]

Casual workers were hired to work on the demesne as and when required. Of the regular farm jobs, they were often employed in weeding and threshing but did other work too.[14] At Petworth in 1347–8 they were employed to get rid of rabbit burrows, cut bracken, dig the garden, cut stubble for thatch, lift stones, dig footings and fell trees. In that year payments were also made to carpenters, masons, painters, plumbers and thatchers.[15] Manorial accounts reveal that some of the casual field workers were women. Apart from tasks like planting beans, binding sheaves and gathering stubble, traditionally carried out by women, they encroached on the male preserve too, being involved in such jobs as hoeing, weeding, haymaking, reaping, threshing, winnowing, carrying the corn and following the plough.[16] The evidence of the sessional rolls, moreover, suggests that in the period after the Black Death such women may have been paid at the same rate as men.[17]

The early modern period

Labour services

By the sixteenth century little remained of the medieval system of holding land in return for labour services. Whilst it was not uncommon for tenants to perform residual services, in general they were far from onerous and were regularly being commuted. At the most, these duties comprised a few days' work a year and, even if carried out, were often undertaken by a substitute paid for the job. The tasks were varied but tended to be associated with periods of high labour requirements, notably at seed time and harvest. Thus, ploughing, reaping, mowing and carting were among the jobs most commonly referred to.

The terms by which individual tenants held their farms, including the provision of labour services, were entered in their leases or in the manor court rolls. At Linley (Shrops.) in 1696 Joseph Sankey's lease stated that he had to provide a labourer to work on the demesne for one day a year, being allowed 15 days' grace to find such a man.[18] When a run of leases or copies survive for a particular property, it may be possible to chart any changes that occurred, especially to pinpoint the demise of labour services. On the other hand, if a set of contemporary estate documents like these are studied, a common pattern might emerge, reflecting the policy of the landowner at that time. On the south Shropshire estate of the Mores of Linley, for instance, leases of the late sixteenth and seventeenth centuries reveal that the tenants' obligation to provide a labourer to work on the demesne for one day a year, noted above, was the normal practice there.[19] Similar information still appears in some surveys and, where it does, it is easier to make comparisons between the farms.

Servants in husbandry

Clearly, apart from the work carried out by farmers and their families, most of the labour requirements on the farms of early-modern England were being met by a paid workforce. Some of the tasks were performed by servants in husbandry, generally people in the their late teens and early twenties, who lived on the farm and who received part of their wages in board and lodgings. They were particularly numerous in the 100 years after the Restoration of 1660, a time of low agricultural prices and scarce labour. They were hired by the year, often at statute or hiring fairs, and did a variety of jobs on the farm. According to Ann Kussmaul, who has written the basic work on the subject, the tasks they did and the wages they received were based upon the sex and age of the servant.[20] Women were involved in dairying, tending to farmyard animals, weeding and tasks ancillary to agriculture such as alemaking and cooking. Men ploughed, harrowed and carted and also looked after draught animals, cattle and sheep.

Contracts made between the two parties were normally verbal (though indentures of agreement were not unknown), and as a result there is less documentation for the practice than might otherwise have been the case. Quarter sessions' records provide a useful source of information; even if the material is of a pathological nature, concentrating on those instances when the system broke down, it does reveal many interesting details. Disputes were often brought before the magistrates because the verbal contracts were recognizable at law.

Occasional censuses record the number of servants working in a locality. Ann Kussmaul based her findings on 25 parish listings made between 1599 and 1831 but detailed research among the archives will reveal others.[21] She did not refer to the 1771 census of Swinderby (Lincs.), for example.[22] There, 16 of the 50 households were headed by farmers, 14 of whom had servants living in with them. On average, they had two servants, one male and one female. As Swinderby was a mixed farming community a substantial labour force was needed, and in pastoral areas other village censuses might reveal a different picture. Many of the farm servants lived in the house, though others were put up in outbuildings. Evidence of the arrangements made by individual farmers for their servants can be found in their probate inventories, which record the chambers in which the servants lodged and the contents of the rooms.

The records of the poor law administration should also be consulted, especially the papers relating to the examination of paupers introduced by the Act of Settlement of 1662. These documents can be found in either parish collections or, because magistrates were involved in making judgements in disputed cases, in the quarter sessions' records. These examinations provide potted biographies of thousands of people claiming parish relief, and among them were agricultural labourers. As one means of obtaining a settlement was by working in a parish for a year, the time spent as a servant in husbandry was carefully noted in the document. Examination papers like these can be put to a number of uses; apart from giving information on the type of work done, they also note the time spend by labourers at a particular place and their movement around the country.

Poor law records include other relevant material. Many pauper children were 'apprenticed' to local farmers, that is, they became agricultural labourers. Evidence for this process is given in the apprenticeship indentures that were drawn up by parish officers. Though hardly comparable to servants in husbandry – they could not move at the end of each year and were invariably used as a means of cheap labour – there were some similarities. They often lived on the farm and many of them acquired useful and marketable skills.

Day labourers

Some servants remained unmarried and cotinued to reside on the farm for the rest of their working lives. Normally, however, servants in husbandry left the household at some point in their mid-twenties, married and established themselves in their own homes.[23] They were now classed as day labourers and, as in the Middle Ages, were paid by the day or by the piece. These labourers faced similar problems to those experienced by their medieval counterparts. A few achieved almost permanent employment, being given a new task to do when they had finished the previous one, but they were in the minority.[24] Skilled workers like ploughmen were prized and could always be sure of a job; other specialists such as herdsmen and shepherds did well too. For most people, however, work was intermittent and seasonal, with winter seen as a particularly difficult time. Fluctuations in the demand for labour in the countryside can be discovered by analysing the information contained in estate and farm accounts. In 1693–4, for instance, Sir John Knatchbull employed five labourers for 226–84 days, three for 121–67 days and ten for 9–51 days. A further 22 were hired at peak times.[25]

The estate workforce

As ever, because it is better documented, more is known of the demesne workforce than of those working for other farmers (even if the latter were beginning to leave accounts and memoranda books). In many ways early-modern estate accounts contain similar information to that found in medieval manorial accounts. The jobs being carried out by farm servants, day labourers and craftsmen are recorded, together with the numbers involved and the rates of pay. Many of the entries are dated, though this might refer to the day on which the account was settled rather than the one on which the task was performed. Thus, on 3 January 1705/6 the Reverend John Crakenthorp of Fowlmere (Cambs.) paid Thomas Watson £1 1s. 8d. for 26 days' work in October, spent ploughing, sowing and carting.[26]

On a number of estates separate accounts were drawn up to record the work done by labourers and their wages. On the estate of the Bridgeman family in Knockin (Shrops.) one such document lists the year's wages due on 1 May 1701; it shows that six men were paid by the year and the rest, a much larger group, were hired by the day. Ditching, however, was assessed at piecework rates, and craftsmen (carpenters, paviers, slaters and masons) were also paid in that way.[27] Another form of record is the individual voucher, a slip of paper noting payment for work done. Sometimes, as on the Earl of Effingham's estate in Surrey, the vouchers were enrolled into receipt books, in which descriptions of the jobs are given, together with the payment and recipient's signature (or mark).[28] Such documents reflect actual wage rates and can therefore be used to compare with official figures. As a result of the Statute of Labourers (1563) justices of the peace in each county periodically had to set maximum wages, and these rates appear in quarter sessions' records.[29]

Diaries, commonplace and memoranda books, and estate correspondence provide additional sources of information. Daniel Eaton, in his letters to his master, the 3rd Earl of Cardigan, reported at length in his dealings with his labourers. He discussed a variety of matters, notably the work the labourers were doing, the difficulties they were causing him, rates of pay and conditions of employment.[30] Henry Best of Elmswell (East Riding) used his farm and memoranda books to record his views on agriculture, as well as the way in which he conducted his business. Most of his workers lived in and one or two ate with the family. At critical times of the year, especially during the hay and corn harvests, he hired other labourers on a day-to-day basis. In summer he obtained workers from the north of Yorkshire moors, putting them up in barns and similar places.[31]

Of course, such evidence looks at the issue of labour from the employer's point of view. For the opinion of labourers, one must turn to records in which they speak for themselves. Settlement examinations, noted above, normally give the bare details, but in other classes of deposition – taken in tithe disputes, quarter sessions and assize cases and at the conciliar courts, for instance – a good deal of incidental material is included.

The agricultural workforce since c. 1750

Over the course of the past two centuries important developments have taken place in agriculture which have changed the
nature of the workforce and the numbers making it up. In
particular, although for well over a century fewer and fewer
people have been employed on farms, output has continued to
grow. Nonetheless, over the whole period the demand for
labour has fluctuated. In many localities, the size of the
workforce increased in the late eighteenth and nineteenth
centuries, due in some measure to the extension of the arable
acreage but also to the diffusion of new labour-intensive
techniques. It has been estimated, for instance, that the
introduction of the Norfolk four-course rotation increased the
workforce by 40 per cent and tripled the number of working
peaks during the year.[32] At the same time industrialization
reduced the pool of labourers available in certain parts of the
country, either by the lure of higher wages or by destroying
rural industry, hitherto an important source of casual work.
By the end of the nineteenth century there may even have been
local shortages of workers, though this shortfall was offset, to
a considerable extent, by the adoption of labour-saving
machinery. During the two world wars, however, the
problem emerged again as a proportion of the workforce
enlisted in the armed services.

The long-term decline in numbers is plainly visible in the
source material, especially in the decennial figures listed in the
abstracts of the national censuses published by the Ministry of
Agriculture, Fisheries and Food. In the first three censuses
(1801–21) general totals were given of the people working
mainly in agriculture; in trade, manufacturing industry and
crafts; and in other occupations. In the first category, however, farmers are not distinguished from labourers. The
census returns of 1831 provide the first meaningful figures for
they include under each parish a section on the number of
labourers in agriculture (though only those aged 20 and over).
From 1841, when information on individuals is recorded, a
much closer analysis is possible.[33] For the situation in
wartime, the papers of the County War Agricultural
Executives can be used for they give details of the means
adopted to make good any deficiencies in the workforce.

The workforce

Some of the labourers recorded in the census returns were not employed on farms in their own parish but worked outside it. In general, the trend was for workers to travel from open parishes, where labour was abundant, to closed parishes, where it was in short supply. As the censuses from 1841 onwards often list the number of labourers working for individual farmers, a rough estimation of the situation in a particular community can be obtained by comparing the total with the recorded size of the labouring population in the parish. The censuses also indicate many of the specialist jobs that were being carried out on the farm, referring to cowmen, carters, ploughmen, thatchers, woodcutters, gelders and many others. Moreover, census abstracts from 1901 divide the agricultural workforce into shepherds, horsemen, cowmen and labourers, providing information unavailable in its original form because of the 100 years' rule. Even so, the typical entry in the returns merely refers to workers as agricultural labourers or farm servants, leaving the reader to guess at the jobs done by each individual.[34] To find out more about these workers and the tasks they were doing, farm and estate accounts or labour books need to be looked at.

Other evidence can be found in those governmental enquiries of the nineteenth century which were set up to investigate the state of agriculture in the country. Some reports dealt with industry in general, and information on labourers has to be gleaned from them in passing. Others were more directly concerned with the workforce, though they often looked at only one aspect of it. Not all of these enquiries were nationwide in their coverage, and local historians should first check in guides to the British Parliamentary Papers to see if their area is included in a particular report. Moreover, it should be noted that the comments in the reports were not necessarily those of labourers but rather the views of middle-class commissioners and observers and, as a result, may not accurately reflect the experience of workers. Where the actual testimony of individual labourers is given, the evidence has greater validity (though it was still sifted and selected before it reached the printed page).

Testimonies in official records like these can be supplemented by oral evidence, recording the reminiscences of people who worked on the farm in the past. Many valuable insights into the way of life of the farm labourer can be gained in this way. Of course, time may have blurred the memory, but according to George Ewart Evans, a writer with considerable experience in oral history, this is not much of a problem in practice. As he observed, 'if you record a man talking about his work, a subject he knows intimately and in great detail, you can rarely fault him'.[35]

Women and children

Women and children continued to augment the workforce. As before, their presence is recorded in estate and farm accounts, but because of the greater volume of material in this period it is now easier to determine the extent and nature of their involvement. At Irely Farm (Glos.) surviving labour books for the years 1869–71 show that, on mixed farms like this, they had an important role to play.[36] The boys helped the carter to do his work which included ploughing, cultivating and harrowing, as well as the carriage of goods. They also performed odd jobs such as bird scaring and picking up stones. The women were employed in the house and garden but also worked in the fields, planting potatoes, hoeing, threshing, haymaking, reaping, swede cleaning and loading manure and tussocks.

In some counties, notably in Northumberland and Dorset, labourers were expected to provide extra hands from amongst their own family whenever the farmer demanded help. Evidence for this practice appears not only in indentures of agreement between the parties but also in newspaper advertisements. In the 1890s the *Dorset County Chronicle* still contained advertisements for labourers 'with a working family'. In the North-east, moreover, the bondage system persisted throughout the nineteenth century; this required married farm workers to provide and maintain an additional female labourer. If no suitable person could be found within the family, another woman had to be hired.[37]

At the turn of the eighteenth century contemporary opinion favoured the employment of women and children, looking upon them as a source of cheap labour to be used as and when required. In the Victorian period, however, attitudes changed as writers and politicians emphasized the corrupting and demoralizing influences of field work.[38] In 1843 a series of reports were made, examining the situation in the South-west,

East Anglia and the North-east, whilst those drawn up in 1867–8 and 1868–9 covered the greater part of the country.[39] Other commissions were established specifically to look into the problem of child labour, and of these the ones which reported in the 1860s are particularly useful.[40] The reports revealed many abuses, especially in the operation of the notorious gang system prevalent in eastern England. Many gangs contained a high proportion of women and children, and witness after witness commented upon the dreadful conditions under which they laboured.[41] As a result of the evidence gathered, the Agricultural Gangs Act was passed in 1867. By its terms children under the age of eight could no longer be employed in public gangs, mixed sex gangs were banned, and gang masters had to be licensed by the magistrates.[42]

The data listed in the national censuses seem to reflect the changing ethos of the time. In 1871 over 58,000 female labourers and farm servants were recorded in England and Wales, a figure which had fallen to less than 12,000 by the end of the century.[43] Research done on Gloucestershire material by Dr Miller, however, suggests that the decline was more apparent than real; in particular, she found that many women described as day labourers in farm and estate accounts were not classified as such in the census returns.[44]

Poverty forced many women out to work. Labourers' children also had to contribute to the family's income as soon as they were able, in spite of the recommendations of the royal commissions and the terms of the education acts. In village schools attendance dropped sharply when crops were ready to be harvested. This is revealed in the attendance figures and in the comments noted by teachers in school log books. At Pershore (Worcs.) the master wrote on 8 September 1893 that many children had been 'kept away all the week to pick hops or blackberries'.[45] Masters often bowed to the inevitable and extended the holidays or closed the school. At Roxwell (Essex) on 23 September 1867 the master noted, 'Opened school, but obliged to close it for another week – harvest not finished therefore children unable to attend'.[46]

Migrant workers

Migrant workers provided another source of labour in the countryside. Farmers had been employing them for centuries but in the 100 years from *c.* 1750 economic circumstances favoured an increase in their numbers. Imbalances between supply and demand meant that some places had to import workers from other parts of the country. Moreover, long distance migration was stimulated by the staggered harvest time as much between individual crops as between different regions. Other migrants were actively sought for permanent jobs. Thus, advertisements were placed in local newspapers in areas where labourers could be found who possessed skills needed elsewhere. On 5 March 1808, for instance, a request from the South was placed in the *Newcastle Courant* for a labourer 'acquainted with drill management'. Another on 5 September 1845 asked for a labourer adept at working with the Aberdeen corn scythe.[47]

Migrant workers, in general, moved from pastoral regions to mixed farming areas where the labour requirements were greater. Of particular importance was the flow of people from the Celtic fringe, notably from Ireland. Unfortunately, the mid nineteenth century censuses do not adequately record the number of casual and migrant workers abroad in the countryside because they were normally compiled in the relatively quiet months of March and April. Only in 1841, when the census was taken in June, do the returns hint at the size of this class of worker. Among the migrant workers in 1841 found by Ted Collins were 177 strangers haymaking at Hendon (Middx.), 182 at Woodford and West Ham (Essex) and 315 at Stone (Kent). In the market gardening parishes of south Essex, moreover, many Irish were at work pea-picking.[48]

The presence of migrant workers can also be seen in traditional sources like farm and estate accounts and labour books. Even if they were not described as such, they might be identified from their surnames. Similarly, examinations recording the life stories of individual workers seeking a settlement continued to be made and can be found among parish and quarter sessions' papers. Evidence for the practice also appears in the *General Views of Agriculture*, in the accounts of farming in the shires published in the *Journal of the Royal Agricultural Society of England* and in local newspapers. Additional material turns up in the reports of the commissions established by Parliament to enquire into aspects of rural society and agriculture. The Royal Commission on the Poor Laws (1834) records the fact that thousands of Irishmen were being passed home because of vagrancy and many of them seem to have been harvest workers.[49] At Preston (Lancs.), for example, 77 reapers were sent back to Ireland in September and October 1832.[50] The seasonal migration of Irish workers peaked at the time of the famine of 1845 but, even if it declined thereafter, many continued to come over to England.[51]

Changes in the nature of the workforce

During the course of the nineteenth century the nature of the workforce changed. In particular, the old practice of living-in servants declined, initially in the South where it occurred early enough to be noted in the *General Views of Agriculture*. In the North the practice continued for much longer and did not finally disappear until the beginning of this century. Local historians interested in finding out about the situation in their own community can do so by looking at the census returns from 1841 onwards as they give personal details. Living-in servants were normally categorized as agricultural servants and were listed as members of the household of their employers. As before, they did not all live under the same roof as the farmer, however; some were put up in barns, lofts and outbuildings and others in bothies, small units of occupation built in the grounds of farms or estates.[52]

The system had certain social and economic advantages and, where the reminiscences of people who experienced it have been recorded, local historians have a first-hand account of the way in which it operated. According to William Rothwell, a retired farmer, writing in the *Ormskirk Advertiser* in January 1913, in the mid nineteenth century 'those servants who boarded in the house, partook at the same table as myself, and sat in the same room of an evening, talking over what we might have done, how we might have done it better and how we could best do the work tomorrow'. Change was under-way, however. By then, he claimed, 'the great body of farmers seem to care little about their servants, except to extract the greatest amount of labour from them'.[53]

As the nineteenth century progressed, the number of casual workers employed as day labourers steadily increased. Those who were retained on an annual basis tended to be skilled workers like horsemen, ploughmen and shepherds.[54] Accounts, labour books and indentures of agreement should be looked at for relevant information, which can be used to build up a picture of the pattern of work in a locality.

Sometimes, labour agreements ran for the whole year, whilst others were of shorter duration or were restricted to the performance of a specific task. A farmer might come to terms with a harvest gang, for instance. At Hall Farm, Great Wilbraham (Cambs.), a company of 15 men were hired to bring in the harvest of 1891 and the agreement that was drawn up not only dealt with wages and conditions of work but also stipulated the farming practices to be observed.[55]

The supply of labour in wartime

In the two world wars the government had the problem of maintaining an adequate labour force on the land. Many workers enlisted and others were called up, even though they benefited from a degree of exemption from the draft. In the counties the situation can be examined through the records of the War Agricultural Executive Committee (WAEC). In the First World War a number of expedients were adopted, many of which were re-introduced in the conflict of the Second World War.[56]

Soldiers formed the largest class of replacement labour, though much of it was unskilled and of limited value. In Somerset, of the 784 men who had reported to the Taunton depot by 25 March 1917, 200 had to be sent back to their units as unsuitable. Nonetheless, the position improved over time; most of the soldiers were willing to learn and gradually became more skilled in farm work. Thus, the committee in Lindsey (Lincs.), commenting on the 226 unskilled men at their disposal, concluded that 'the majority are becoming more useful as time progresses – the efforts of certain farmers in training these men having been most praiseworthy'.[57] Prisoners-of-war were also used. After initial reluctance, a fact noted in the minutes and reports of a number of county committees, they were eventually introduced onto the farms. In general, the scheme proved beneficial; most of the men were reliable workers and some proved to be a positive asset. The report of the Lindsey committee, dated 31 March 1918, noted that, 'The prisoners are specially selected agriculturalists, and are engaged in farm work, and in ditching, hedging, &c. They are reported in all cases to be working satisfactorily, and giving no trouble.'[58]

Women and children were pressed into service too. In 1916 Women's War Agricultural Committees (WWACs) were set up in each county to promote the employment of women in agriculture. The following year the Women's Land Army was formed, designed to provide a skilled yet mobile labour force which could be moved from place to place wherever needed and which would also encourage village women to come forward in greater numbers. In the counties selection commit-tees were established to interview candidates and comments made on the individual applicants survive in the minute books of the boards. Sometimes, the middle-class prejudices of the panel shows through. B.H., interviewed by the Hertfordshire committee on 26 April 1918, was described as 'the worst type of munitions worker. Flashy, and very yellow as to hair. Quite inexperienced, except as to horses, her father was a dealer in them. Not suitable.' This was a pity because people skilled in dealing with horses were in short supply! The minutes and reports of the WWACs reveal much more, not only indicating prevailing attitudes towards women's work but also recording the training they received, the jobs they did and the standards they achieved in them.[59]

Schoolchildren were another valuable resource and were seen as such by the WAECs. In January 1916, for example, the Oxford committee resolved to put pressure on the Education Committee to free children to work on the farm 'at certain periods of agricultural activity'.[61] On 26 June 1917 the labour sub-committee in Shropshire reported a meeting with a Mr Woolcombe, a representative of the National Service Depart-ment, who discussed with them a scheme for getting public and secondary schoolboys to help with the hay and corn harvests.[62]

The evidence contained in the minutes and reports of the First World War committees can be complemented by the material included in the Parliamentary *Report on Wages and Conditions of Employment in Agriculture*, published in 1919.[63] Many of the deponents were farmers who spoke of their experiences in the war. Their assessment of the work done by replacement labour was varied; it was often felt to be inferior, though there seems to have been some agreement that it had improved with time. In Shropshire the report concluded that the workers had been insufficient in number and of poorer quality than the regular labour force. One Shropshire farmer complained of a soldier allocated to him, 'One of the men I got was a piano-tuner; I could knock nothing into him.'[64]

Wages and labour organizations

Wages in agriculture were generally much lower than those which workers in other industries could obtain. They were highest in areas where farmers had to compete with manufacturing industries. Farm and estate accounts reveal that labourers did best in parts of Lancashire and worst in parts of Dorset and Wiltshire with no alternative forms of employment. Skilled men continued to be paid at the highest rates; on the Blount estate at Mapledurham (Oxon.) the head carter earned 15s. 0d. a week, whilst general labourers received 12s. 0d. or 13s. 0d.[65] Many workers still obtained a proportion of their wages in kind and the servants in husbandry their board and lodgings. This was not a new situation, however, and the means of remuneration, together with some of the sources that can be used to analyse labourers' wages, have already been dealt with. Additional information can be found in the *General Views of Agriculture* and among the Parliamentary Papers. The subject of wages was one which particularly interested nineteenth-century governments, and a number of commissions were set up to look into the matter.[66]

The issue was obviously of great concern to labourers too, and in this period various attempts were made by the workers to improve their lot. The earliest type of organization took the form of friendly societies which aimed at providing financial and medical help to their members in sickness and in old age. Such bodies had existed before the mid eighteenth century but it was only subsequently that they became numerous and flourished. The Poor Law Amendment Act of 1834 acted as a further stimulus, as the working class saw the friendly societies as a means of self-help which would keep them out of the workhouse. Many local societies were founded but, often under-funded, they soon folded. Nonetheless, by the end of the nineteenth century one or two national societies, notably the Oddfellows and the Foresters, had emerged with numerous branches around the country. Evidence of their activities appears in the minute books and accounts which were occasionally kept, though until the Friendly Societies Act of 1875 these bodies tended to be poorly managed. Local newspapers also reported the events that they organized, especially the annual feasts which formed such an important element of their social life.[67]

The nineteenth century also saw the development of

agricultural trade unionism, culminating in the formation of the National Agricultural Labourers' Union (NALU) in 1872 under the leadership of Joseph Arch.[68] For a couple of years the union enjoyed considerable success, and wage rates were raised in many parts of the country, often without the need for the labourers to go on strike. Farm and estate accounts provide the details. On Butler Farm near Blandford (Dorset) in 1872 the weekly wage for labourers was 9s. 0d. and had been fixed at that rate since the mid 1860s. After the harvest of that year, however, pay rose to 10s. 0d. or 11s. 0d. and peaked in the spring of 1873 at 12s. 0d.[69] Unfortunately, this favourable state of affairs did not last long; farmers formed their own defence associations, and when the trial of strength came in 1874 the NALU had to admit defeat.[70]

The earlier history of the movement can be traced through various sources. Labourers who formed illegal combinations like the one at Tolpuddle (Dorset) in 1833–4, were tried at the quarter sessions and assizes and their cases recorded in the papers of the courts. The outcome of such trials was printed in newspapers; indeed, the publicity given to the harsh treatment meted out to the 'Tolpuddle Martyrs' led to their eventual pardon and return home from Australia.[71] Newspapers reported other occasions when workers combined to press for the reform of abuses. Meetings were held to agitate for the abolition of the corn laws, for instance. According to the local press, one gathering which assembled at Bremhill (Wilts.) in February 1846 comprised 1,500 labourers and their wives. Naturally, the development of agricultural trade unionism attracted the attention of journalists. In an article published in *Jackson's Oxford Journal* on 9 March 1872 it was reported that there had been 'a good deal of agitation among labourers in the Banbury district and that as a result of their action a 1s. 0d. rise in wages had been achieved'.[72]

The union also generated its own records, which mainly consisted of accounts and minutes. A strike fund had to be collected and money paid to locked-out labourers, and this required a considerable amount of administrative activity. Thus, in the minute book of the Oxford district of the NALU, an entry dated 14 April 1874 notes, 'remit to Leamington £87 – 3 – 1 which we have collected as lock out fund'.[73] Farm and estate correspondence provide another source of evidence, though, of course, it portrays the struggle from the other side.

Summary

Changes in the nature of the workforce have undoubtedly had an impact on the efficiency of farming. In the Middle Ages, for instance, the commutation of services was at least partly due to the greater effectiveness of hired workers over customary labour. In more recent times dramatic improvements have been made in output through the process of mechanization. After some initial opposition machines seem to have been accepted largely because they were not brought into general use until there was a need for them. Thus, the late nineteenth century was a critical period, a time when a growing shortage of labour provided a favourable climate for their adoption. Much is known about the agricultural workforce – their numbers, wages and jobs and the ways in which they responded to changes outlined in this chapter. Indeed, by examining poor law records, especially settlement papers, the local historian can learn a great deal about their life and work. Oral evidence, recording the experience of people who actually performed the tasks on the farm, further fills in the picture. As with other areas of agricultural research, the demesne workforce is the best documented one, though evidence of those employed by other farmers does improve over time as the surviving material becomes more comprehensive and wide ranging.

Chapter Eight

TOOLS, EQUIPMENT AND FARM BUILDINGS

The Middle Ages

Tools, equipment and farm buildings on the demesne

To help them in their activities, medieval farmers and labourers had a variety of tools and equipment. Some items were in use in all parts of the century but others had a regional concentration. Improvements were made over the course of time, too. Inevitably, because of the value of the manorial accounts as a source, most is known about the demesne. They provide details of not only the implements, tools and vehicles employed there but also the draught animals used. Lists of equipment may be given, whilst other entries refer to costs incurred in using the implements or in making or repairing them.

To manufacture or repair ploughs most of the money was spent on iron and steel, not wood, and consequently it is difficult to know to what extent ploughs with heavy mould boards had taken over from ards or scratch ploughs in the period after the Norman Conquest. The presence on the demesne of large plough teams suggests that they had done so but little positive proof can be found.[1] On the other hand, one can normally tell if wheeled, foot or swing ploughs were being used because the wheels and feet were expensive enough items to warrant specific mention in the accounts.[2] When references to each type of plough are plotted on a map, certain regional variations emerge. Wheeled ploughs predominated in the South-east and in eastern Norfolk, foot ploughs mainly in the South-west (from Hampshire in the east to the west Midlands in the north) and swing and foot ploughs together in the North.[3]

The accounts show that demesne farmers used a range of vehicles. The most common type was the cart (*carecta*), a two-wheeled vehicle drawn by horses. Its distribution was virtually nationwide, though there was a tendency for it to be supplemented or replaced in the North and the West by the wain (*plaustrum*). Outside these regions particular concentrations of wains occurred in Sussex and southern Kent. It was, like the cart, a two-wheeled vehicle but was much larger and was pulled by oxen. The term *carrus*, when referring to a farm vehicle, indicates another two-wheeled wain drawn by oxen. Its design was similar to that of the *plaustrum*, and the two words seem to have been interchangeable. Other types of vehicles are recorded in the documents but none was as important as carts or wains.[4]

Both horses and oxen were used for the draught but apart from regional variations in their use, there was often a distinction between the jobs they carried out. In the preparation of the seed-bed, for instance, horses were more likely to be engaged in harrowing than in ploughing.[5] Occasionally, the accounts list horses kept for specific tasks (for harrowing, at Belper, Derbys., in 1256–7) but, in general, they had other duties too. In the centuries after the Conquest, moreover, horses took over much of the haulage work on the demesne. A calculation based upon the frequency within which horse-drawn carts or ox-drawn wains are mentioned in the accounts suggests that three-quarters of the demesne haulage was being performed by horses at the end of the thirteenth century. In spite of a modest recovery by ox-hauled vehicles in the next 100 years the proportion was still over two-thirds at the end of the fourteenth century. At the end of the Middle Ages oxen still retained their leading position as plough animals, but in areas like East Anglia, the Chilterns and the Home Counties all-horse teams were making an appearance, whilst mixed teams were spreading out more widely across eastern and south-eastern England.

This pattern reflects agricultural and geographical differences between the regions. Areas of horse-draught tended to be located in places where intensive husbandry practices were being carried on and where fodder was readily available. Horses were particularly adept at working in districts with light and stony soils, for their strength, speed and agility made them a more efficient form of power. On stiff, heavy clays, however, oxen did comparatively better and thus more were kept there. They cost less to feed and did not depreciate so much in value after their working life was over. After fattening, they could be sold for a considerable sum, whereas horses were worth very little. Local historians should, of course, keep such considerations in mind when seeking to explain the situation in their own communities and should therefore bring a number of different sources to bear on the question.

Among the other expenses recorded in manorial accounts are those for the construction and repair of farm and other buildings on the demesne. The information appears in the charge side of the account, in either the list of payments to labourers and craftsmen or a specific section on building costs. The expenditure is often itemized in great detail, revealing, for instance, the number of nails and laths used.[6] The data provides us with evidence on such matters as the size of individual buildings and the materials out of which they were constructed. Surveys and extents should also be looked at, as should the Hundred Rolls of 1279. These sources are not as detailed as accounts but do indicate the number and type of farm buildings on the demesne.

The sources are particularly good for the study of mills. From surveys and extents (including the Hundred Rolls), for instance, one can find out roughly when windmills were introduced into an area. The first ones were constructed in the late twelfth century, though they took some time to spread around the country. They complemented rather than replaced watermills, and on many demesnes there were both sorts. At Kempsey in 1299 separate entries record a watermill (*molendinum aquaticum*) and a windmill (*molendinum ad ventum*).[7] Some indication of the size and output of individual mills may perhaps be gained by looking at the valuation given to them. Manorial accounts provide us with other evidence. Because the costs incurred in repairing and replacing various parts of the machinery are included, one can learn about the workings of the mill.[8] The Domesday Book is another source of information, if a somewhat unreliable one. Some 6,000 mills are listed in the survey, though the count is complicated by the number entered as fractions (because they were in divided ownership). At that time, some manors had several mills, whereas in others none were recorded. This does not necessarily mean that the tenants had to go elsewhere to have their corn ground (though the value given to some mills suggests that they catered for a wider area than the manor). Many had clearly been overlooked or omitted – there must have been more than six mills in Cornwall![9]

Tools and equipment used by medieval peasantry

For peasant holdings one can use those inventories which occasionally turn up in such sources as manor court rolls, inquisitions and manorial accounts.[10] There, one can find references to tools, equipment and draught animals. Particularly useful are the set of *principia*, descriptions of the holdings and possessions of unfree tenants written in the manor court rolls.[11] A list of goods belonging to a Wolverley (Worcs.) man in 1374, for instance, reveals that he had a cart, a plough with coulter and plough share, and a harrow. His hand tools comprised a scythe, two axes, a spade, a flail, a mattock, a fork for the sheaves, a bush hook and a gimlet.[12] Other incidental references to equipment appear in the court rolls from time to time, perhaps because an item had been stolen, used illegally to cut down branches or dig up turf or even employed as a murder weapon. Tools and equipment also served as heriots if no better item could be taken. Surveys and extents provide additional evidence, especially of the equipment and vehicles belonging to peasants used on the demesne when discharging their obligations to their lord. Thus, at Crawley (Hants.) *c.* 1280, among the services that Robert at Mere, a half-virgater, had to perform was the carriage of hay with his horse and cart (*cum equo et carecta*).[13] The pattern that emerges is very similar to that found on the demesne: the most common vehicle was the cart, followed by the two sorts of wain.[14]

An interesting contrast with the demesne can be seen when looking at the draught animals used by the peasantry. Surveys and accounts indicate that, as on the demesne, harrowing and haulage were increasingly being performed by horses but ploughing was a different matter. In fact, peasants were more likely to use horses for this task than were demesne farmers. According to John Langdon, the determinant was largely an economic one and depended upon the size of the holding. Consequently, horse-ploughing tended to be the preserve of the small farmer in areas where their more substantial neighbours (virgaters and even half-virgaters) were using oxen. Surveys do not always specify the function of horses in peasant teams employed on the demesne but this conclusion can be reached by looking at other sources. Inventories, lay subsidies and manor court rolls all refer to peasant animals and, in spite of their limitations, these records give some indication of the type of draught animals they owned. Smaller farmers preferred horses because of their greater flexibility. They could not afford to keep a variety of animals to carry out the different jobs that had to be done, for either themselves or their lord, and horses, therefore, were the obvious choice.[15]

The early modern period

Early-modern farmers and labourers used tools and equipment which would have been familiar to their medieval forebears. As Dr Kerridge has observed, 'mechanization formed no part of the early modern agricultural revolution'. Nonetheless, because we have a new source of information available to us in the form of the probate inventory, more is now known about them. Most of the equipment was associated with arable farming and, as a result, inventories of mixed farmers tend to contain longer and more comprehensive lists of items. When Richard Clary, a yeoman from Writtle (Essex) died in the winter of 1693/4, he possessed a wide range of tools and equipment which serve to indicate the type of farm gear being used at the time.[17]

Richard Clary had sown 16 acres of wheat and 14 acres of peas in the fields of Writtle in the year he died and had prepared another 13 acres for barley. The reference to a seed cob in his inventory demonstrates that he was sowing the seed broadcast. Local farmers were also hand-drilling their seed for in 1670 William Irons senior left a pair of setters (dibblers).[18] By the middle of the eighteenth century a number of mechanized drills had been invented, notably that of Jethro Tull, but they had been adopted by only a small number of gentlemen-enthusiasts. They do not appear in the inventories of ordinary farmers of the time, and if any references are to be found they will turn up in estate accounts and correspondence.

To prepare the ground for the seed Richard Clary used ploughs and harrows (and presumably a clodding beetle or roller, though none was recorded by the appraisers of his goods). There were several contemporary ploughs and the ones used by individual farmers depended on such factors as the nature of the soil and terrain, and local custom. In general, they can be grouped into four categories: the double-wheeled; the single-wheeled and foot ploughs; ploughs with neither wheels nor feet; and the dutch or plain Dutch plough.[19] Occasionally, appraisers specified the type of plough being used but normally, as in Richard Clary's case, they did not.

Hand tools	1 hatchet, 1 pickaxe, 1 grubbing axe, 1 mattock, 1 bill, 1 spade, 1 shovel, 1 casting shovel, 1 dung fork, 2 rakes, 4 weed hooks.
Harvest tools	1 scythe, 5 sickles, 1 peas hook, 2 hay forks, 4 forks.
Implements to prepare ground	Plough timber, 1 timber chain, 2 ploughs with shares, coulters, chains and whipple-trees, 5 harrows.
Containers and sieves	2 corn hutches, 1 seed cob, 3 sieves, 2 chaff sieves, 1 caving sieve, 1 riddle, 1 bushel, 1 half-bushels
Farm vehicles	1 carriage, 1 load cart, 2 dung carts, 1 waggon, 1 pair of wheels, ropes, 1 ladder, winch-pins, 1 wheelbarrow.
Draught horses	5 horses, collars, halters, harness for ploughs and cart for 1 team being two sets, 1 pannell.
Processing dairy products	In the dairy: 1 little table, 1 form, 1 cheese press, 1 milk stand, 1 churn & staff, 6 shelves, 6 cheese moulds, 5 cheese breads, 3 milk pans, 2 trays, 1 hand dish, 1 frying pan, 2 sieves, 5 pots, 1 pan, 1 butter basket, and other implements.
Processing drink	In the little buttery: 1 hogshead, 4 shelves, 5 pots, 1 firkin, and other small implements. In the great buttery: 2 hogsheads, 1 stall, 1 funnel, 1 hop sieve, 2 tap hoses, 4 dishes, 1 dozen trenchers.
Processing wool	1 wheel.

Table 1: *Farm and Processing Equipment in the Inventory of Richard Clary, Yeoman, of Writtle (Essex), Appraised 14 February 1693/4.*

For the draught Richard used horses exclusively. Farmers elsewhere were also turning to horses to pull the plough as well as to draw the harrow and cart. By the end of the period, therefore, the area where all-horse teams were the norm had expanded from its medieval base.[20] In Shropshire, for instance, inventories reveal that oxen were the only plough animals in the mid sixteenth century. By the 1740s, however, horses had made considerable inroads into the areas of ox-draught, especially in light-soil districts.[21] Inventories further show that the trend was a general one and not, as in the Middle Ages, confined to smaller farmers. Indeed, estate records such as accounts, memoranda books and correspondence emphasize the importance of horses on the demesne. In addition, large landowners, with their greater resources, were more likely to keep horses for specific jobs. Thus, draught, cart and plough horses, classified as such, often appear in the accounts.[22]

Horse power became more effective over time, especially in the period after the Restoration. On demesnes and the larger farms bigger and more powerful horses, the result of a century of inter-breeding with stock from the Low Countries, were being introduced.[23] Gradually these animals spread across the country, easing such tasks as soil-preparation and the marketing of produce because of their greater strength. These horses can be recognized in the relevant documentation – inventories, accounts and toll books – by their high value (£5 or more) and by their size (15 hands plus).

Another major technological development, discernible in Richard Clary's inventory, is the waggon, a heavy four-wheeled vehicle introduced onto the farms of lowland England in the mid seventeenth century. They were amongs the largest and most costly of early-modern farm vehicles and as such were monopolized by prosperous farmers who used them as bulk transporters of produce.[24] Among English farmers as a whole carts still predominated and were to be found all over the country. Judging from the price, some carts may have been similar in size to the waggons, perhaps representing an adaptation designed to meet the demand for a two-wheeled vehicle with a greater carrying capacity. Richard's load cart at £6 10s. 0d. was worth more than his waggon (£5). In general, however, carts cost half the price of waggons. Muck carts, as in Richard's inventory, were usually specified as such; they were more solidly built than most farm carts, owing to the type of load carried. To increase the capacity of carts, especially at harvest time, 'ladders' were added to the sides to enable the load to overhang.

Of the other vehicles, wains were still numerous in early-modern England, with a distribution pattern similar to that found in the Middle Ages. They were smaller than their medieval counterparts, however, and, in spite of thir survival from an earlier time, undoubtedly declined in popularity in the second half of the period. Tumbrils, on the other hand, continued to be employed at the same rate as before. Many carts and wains had detachable bodies, reflected in the numerous references in inventories to cart bodies and wheels. The price of wheels varied considerably, the most valuable ones being those shod with iron, as this not only involved extra work and material but also prolonged their life. More rudimentary were the sleds or sledges, which had no wheels but were dragged along the ground.

Evidence of the vehicles used on the demesne appears in estate records, sometimes in the same form as it had done in the medieval period. Thus, in estate accounts they are referred to if the servants had used them to transport goods, if they had been bought or sold, or if they had been repaired. The Reverend John Crakanthorp of Fowlmere (Cambs.), for instance, paid to have a cart ladder made and his waggon shafts mended in August 1706.[25] Farm and memoranda books like those belonging to Henry Best provide another sources. On his East Riding estate in the mid seventeenth century wains were the most common farm vehicle. When bringing in the winter corn three wains were used, with a forker and a loader to a vehicle. Each wain brought in six or seven loads a day. The corn off the estate was sent to market on the backs of horses, normally at least eight horse-loads at a time.[26]

Much processing of agricultural goods was carried out in the homes of farmers and other members of the rural community. From his inventory, we can see that Richard Clary made cheese and brewed his own beer. He also had a spinning wheel in the little kitchen with which his wife and daughters would have spun wool into yarn. Such references are commonplace and can be found in inventories from all parts of the country. However, where a large proportion of the inventory-leaving population was involved in a particular activity, especially if they possessed comparatively large stocks of commodity, one can presume that it was a specialism of the area.

From his inventory we can see that Richard Clary had special rooms set aside to make his cheese and beer. He also had a number of farm buildings, in which he stored his corn and housed his animals. Their names – stable, cart house, barn and little barn – are self-explanatory and in them the appraisers listed the goods we would expect to find there. However, apart from generalizations like 'the little barn', such people rarely give details of the buildings. Estate surveys sometimes give this information, noting down the rooms in tenants' houses and the walling and roofing materials of the homes, barns and outbuildings. Their general size may be indicated too, the buildings being described in terms of the number of bays they contained. Maps might show the building in pictorial form, though allowance should be made for artistic licence. Estate accounts, like their medieval counterparts, still include details of money spent in constructing and repairing farm buildings. For parsonages one has the evidence of the glebe terriers which describe church property in a parish. The ones I have looked at (mainly for Leicestershire, Shropshire and Worcestershire) merely state size and bays of buildings but others elsewhere contain more information. In 1727 the glebe terrier of Honeychurch (Devon), after describing the parsonage, refers to the outhouses in the following terms.[27]

> One Barn adjoining to the east end of the dwelling house in length about twenty four foot the walls of earth & covered with reed. One Stallhouse usually called the Shippin adjoining to the west end of the dwelling house twelve foot in length the walls of earth & covered with reed.

Incidentally, this reference informs us that in the North and the West the tradition of the longhouse or shippon survived through the early-modern period. In this arrangement the accommodation for the humans and for the animals was under the same roof.

Technological advances since c. 1750

The mechanization of agriculture

Overall, the most far-reaching developments in agricultural equipment in the last 200 or so years have been those concerned with the mechanization of farming and the application of new power sources to the machines. Improvements took place in hand-tool technology too. In the early nineteenth century, for instance, the more effective scythe and bagging hook replaced the sickle and reap hook, thereby speeding up the task of getting in the harvest.[28] Moreover, the substitution of cast iron for wood, stone and wrought iron increased the durability and efficiency of the implements.[29] Considerable interest was also shown in the design of equipment, notably that of the plough. Of the many models on sale in the eighteenth century, the Rotherham plough, a swing plough with a curved mouldboard, was the best known and by 1800 had been widely adopted in northern and eastern England. In the following decades, moreover, a growing number of farmers exchanged their wooden ploughs for iron ones. At the same time, improved harrows and rollers, in appearance very similar to twentieth-century models, were introduced.[30]

From the middle of the nineteenth century the pace of mechanization quickened, especially on large mixed farms. By the 1850s threshing machines were being used in southern and eastern England once more, aided by the development of portable models. Seed drills were becoming more popular too, and mechanical harvesters had begun to appear. American reaping machines were displayed at the Great Exhibition of 1851, and in the late 1870s two-thirds of the country's corn was being cut and harvested by machine. In the last quarter of the century farming efficiency was further improved by the introduction of self-binding reapers, double furrow ploughs and potato planters.[31] On pastoral farms hay harvesters came into use. Some were simple mowers but others had the facility to reap the corn as well as mow the hay.[32] Rowers and tedders were employed to make hay, although they proved to be less popular with Victorian farmers than horse-drawn hay rakes, a device which speeded up the gathering of the crop.[33] In the twentieth century progress accelerated with the development of machines such as combined harvesters and mechanized milking parlours.

Revolutionary changes also occurred in motive power. The debate over the use of horses and oxen continued to exercise the minds of farmers and agricultural writers. Reporters in the *General Views of Agriculture* discussed the relative merits of both animals but came to no overall agreement. Oxen remained the principal draught animals in a number of areas throughout the nineteenth century and survived long enough to have their photographs taken pulling the plough. Horses steadily took over, however, as an examination of sources such as farm and estate accounts, auctioneers' records and newspaper advertisements reveals. In the early nineteenth century animals provided the main power source for agricultural machinery but in the following 50 years steam power was gradually applied to it. Some tasks were more easily converted than others; steam ploughing required regular shaped fields cleared of stones and therefore presented a greater problem than did steam threshing.[34] Finally, in the twentieth century tractors took over, though the transition was not brought about quickly and horses remained an important source of power until after the Second World War. The use of tractors spread slowly in the 1930s and in 1942 a mere 100,000 were at work on the farms of England and Wales.[35]

Labourers and mechanization

Before the new implements could prove their worth, labourers had to be convinced of their utility. They were also concerned about innovations which might take away their livelihood. When Sir John Delaval, then at London, sent two ploughs to the agent of his Northumberland estate, they did not find favour with his workers. As the agent reported, the labourers put forward all sorts of reasons for not using them. In this respect, the process of mechanization was partly delayed by the opposition of the workforce, though in some parts of the country the availability of cheap labour provides an additional explanation. One of the main objectives of the so-called Captain Swing riots of 1830 was the elimination of threshing machines which threatened to reduce the amount of work they could obtain in winter.[36]

The views of the rioters can be found in the letters they sent to farmers and landowners, many of which have been deposited in estate and farm collections in county record offices. Other evidence occurs in quarter sessions' records and consists of the testimony of witnesses and accused. From these accounts a picture of events can be pieced together. Local newspapers also covered the riots and their aftermath, whilst at a national level the Home Office papers contain reports from the localities.[38] After the trouble, which was concentrated in areas of plentiful labour in eastern and southern England, the use of threshing machines declined. Many farmers made the calculation that with labour cheap the introduction of threshing machines was not worth the cost in unrest and a possible increase in the poor rate.[39]

The late nineteenth century was a period when some of the old constraints against the use of machinery were broken down. In certain areas labour was becoming scarce and more expensive. Even the labourers were more amenable. In particular, with more winter work available, workers readily gave up threshing, one of the most tedious of jobs on the farm.[40] From the farmers' point of view, mechanization freed them from reliance on casual and migrant labour, though the situation varied regionally. In 1853, for instance, the *Farmer's Magazine* reported that Middlesex farmers had refused to adopt mowing machines, fearing opposition from their labourers. In the East Riding, on the other hand, reaping machines came into use because it was said that 'it would only do the work which is at present done by the Irish'.[41] Agitation on behalf of the National Agricultural Labourers' Union in the early 1870s provided another stimulus, a development reflected in newspaper reports of the harvest having been safely gathered in as a result of the purchase of machinery.[42] Estate correspondence reveals a similar picture. In 1891 the agent of the Speke estate (Lancs.) wrote to his master to inform him of the trouble he was having with his Irish labourers. Nine men, he noted had withheld their labour at Mount Pleasant Farm but, as he had acquired a potato digger, he was able to get the work done.[43] The introduction of machinery had an impact on labour costs. An analysis of estate accounts and labour books shows that the effect was often dramatic. On the Speke estate the wages bill on the home farm dropped from £671 in 1892 to £523 in 1898.[44]

Mechanization and the documents

The process of mechanization on the farms of England can be examined by looking at a number of documents. The best, of course, are those which appear in bulk and on a regular basis, providing a sufficient amount of material to make conclusions derived from them statistically valid. Unfortunately, sets of probate inventories, which peter out in the mid eighteenth century, can no longer be used, though a few exist for a later date. To these can be added the inventories of farm stock and equipment which were made from time to time as part of the business of estate management. At Holkham (Norfolk) in 1817, for instance, an inventory reveals that the Earl of Leicester had on his demesne, among other things, two threshing and four winnowing machines, seven drills, two machines for sowing broadcast and 14 wheel-ploughs.[45]

Such inventories form a part of estate collections and should be used with other relevant material. Accounts, as before, should record the purchase of equipment and machinery: in 1853 the Earl of Sefton's agent bought a horse-drawn reaping machine costing £10 for use on the home farm at Croxteth Park (Lancs.).[46] Operational costs should also be included, though these might appear in special labour books. The views of landowners and agents towards mechanization can be found in the correspondence which passed between them, especially if one or the other was a committed improver. James Loch, the chief steward of the Leveson-Gower family in the early nineteenth century, was one such man and he was determined to initiate changes in local farming practices. He wrote down his views in books and in letters to farmers and agents, as well as to his master and they included comments on such diverse matters as the introduction of new crops, the use of better fertilizers, scientific breeding, mechanization and improved equipment. He also advocated the employment of lighter carts, the adoption of stronger harrows and the use of more horse-hoes, straw-cutters, turnip-slicers and scufflers. He enthusiastically introduced threshing machines onto the estate, writing in 1820 that in the previous seven years 37 farmhouses with their outbuildings had been erected, virtually all of which had had a threshing machine provided.[47]

One of Loch's experiments, set up to assess the relative merits of drilling seeds and sowing broadcast, was reported in William Pitt's *General View of the Agriculture of the County of Shropshire*, published in 1817. Information like this regularly turns up in these reports. Because correspondents were specifically asked to comment upon the implements in use in their counties, they tended to highlight those innovations they could find. Thus, as most counties published more than one report, they can be used in a general way to indicate the diffusion of a particular machine, at least among the large landowners, the people most commonly interviewed by the writers. Care must be taken, of course, because of the impressionistic nature of much of the material and the variable quality of the reports but they still remain a useful source of information and technological advance.[48]

Of more general application are the records of auctioneers. In particular, local historians need to look at disposal sales rather than to the sales of agricultural produce and stock for they were more likely to deal with equipment. Such sales, as noted in an earlier chapter, occurred at atypical times in the history of an enterprise and therefore may offer only a partial and perhaps misleading picture. It depends on how much had already 'disappeared' before the sale had been organized. Nonetheless, the documents list farm equipment in detail and can be used to date the spread of certain innovations. At the sale of stock belonging to Mr Richard Smith of Ludstone Farm (Shrops.) in October 1845 hand-tools and horse tack were disposed of as well as draught animals, vehicles, equipment and machinery.[49]

It should be emphasized once more that auction records should be studied in conjunction with local newspapers since auctioneers regularly advertised farm sales in them. The source is a daunting one to use but as sales tended to be concentrated at Lady Day and Michaelmas, in practice the task is not such a difficult one. Similar details of equipment are given as those that appear in sales books. The evidence might exaggerate the trend towards mechanization, however: an analysis based upon entries in the *Ormskirk Advertiser* reveals that the larger farms are over-represented in the samples. In south-west Lancashire, the area covered by the newspaper, the first mower in the sampled sale notices appeared in 1860. By 1881 three-quarters of the notices examined contain references to mowers or to combined mowing and reaping machines. The introduction of the self-binder came later – it is first referred to in the *Ormskirk Advertiser* in 1900. By 1913 the newspaper could report that 'wherever one may travel on the Ormskirk district it is rare indeed for a mower and reaper to be seen at work'. This example shows that newspaper references to farm machinery are not confined solely to sales notices. Correspondents also reported on the use of machinery, perhaps having been present at the trial of a new piece of equipment. Other references in newspapers consist of advertisements placed by manufacturers as a means of selling their wares.[50]

The supply of equipment and power in wartime

The records of the county agricultural executive committees (WAECs) indicate the problems of maintaining an adequate supply of draught animals and machinery. In the First World War there was a particular demand for draught horses because of not only the requirements of the army but also the government's ploughing-up campaign of 1917–18. As a result, fewer animals were available at precisely the time when more were needed. In June 1917, therefore, the government introduced the 'Sale of Horses' order, banning sales of farm horses without a licence from the county committee. In Norfolk 8,500 licences were granted in the period the system operated and only 33 applications were refused. These licences, where they survive, contain details on individuals and therefore are of particular value to the local historians.[51]

To make good any local deficiency the government, through the agency of the Food Production Department (FPD), provided thousands of horses for hire, together with ploughmen, harnesses and equipment. Between September 1917 and June 1918 the number of horses hired rose from 1,200 to 11,000. The West Sussex committee alone ordered 1,600 horses and 800 ploughmen. This information can be placed in context by relating it to the parish total recorded in the agricultural returns from 1869 (when horses were first noted) and in the censuses of horses taken in 1917, 1918, 1920, 1924 and 1934. Inconsistencies in the data, however, especially in the censuses, which are badly categorized and contain omissions, make them difficult sources to use. As Keith Chivers, the author of the standard work on the shire horse, has noted, 'The more one studies the five census, the more unreliable they manifestly appear on the record of the numerical strength of various types of horse'. Readers should therefore look at his appraisal of the figures before analysing the material for themselves.[53]

The WAECs also dealt with the provision of agricultural equipment and machinery. Censuses were taken of equipment on the farms of individual counties and attempts were made to improve the stock. In 1917–18, because of the food crisis, the FPD built up a store of equipment which could be hired out to farmers through the agency of the county committees. In Northamptonshire the committee obtained 156 ploughs, 40 disc harrows, 63 horse harrows, 34 disc drills, 41 cultivators,

55 rollers and 86 binders in this way. The committee also supervised the use of steam ploughing and threshing machines, often establishing joint boards with contractors who did most of the work. In Hertfordshire a sub-committee met each week to discuss applications for steam ploughing and to organize the deployment of equipment.[54]

In every county a machinery sub-committee was set up, mainly to deal with the supply of tractors. Many were hired from the government, operating through the FPD. Some were private machines commandeered by the government – in Hertfordshire in April 1917 13 of the 15 loaned out belonged to individual farmers – but over time the FPD built up its own stock. At first the FPD controlled affairs because of the inexperience of most members of the county committees.[55] Nonetheless, local officials gradually came to assume greater responsibility, drawing up contracts with farmers, discussing costs and planning timetables for the use of machines. They met a certain amount of resistance among farmers, who were perhaps wary of new-fangled machines: in Shropshire the committees had to threaten the occupier at Acton Round Farm with eviction if he did not apply for a motor plough within a week.[56]

Farm buildings

In this period farm buildings underwent a remarkable transformation. We have seen that earlier farmsteads contained a number of outbuildings, but as Roy Brigden states, 'farms were commonly made up of an amalgam of buildings that had accumulated over the centuries to no logical plan, were unsuited to present conditions and were, in any case, falling into disrepair'.[57] During the course of the nineteenth century a more scientific approach was adopted to the farm and the layout of farm buildings, prompted, so it seems, by developments in efficiency which were taking place in industry.[58] Consequently, a great deal of reorganization and rebuilding was undertaken, with the aim of improving efficiency and increasing output. This included provision for power sources as agriculture began to mechanize, reflected in the construction of wheelhouses for horse gins, the cutting of leets for water wheels or the erection of a building to house a steam engine.

Large landowners took the lead in such matters. Once

more, therefore, estate records provide us with some of the best examples of the developments that were being carried on. The audit books of the Coke family of Holkham Hall (Norfolk) illustrate this point. They are particularly full and contain detailed information on building improvements on the estate. A survey of expenditure on tenants' farms reveals two phases of activity, one before 1840 and the other after 1860. In the first period capital expenditure was concentrated on the house and premises, whereas in the second one money was largely spent on improving the animal accommodation. The value of estate maps and plans in this period should be stressed too.[59] Increasingly, plans were drawn up to accompany proposed improvements and thus provide a detailed cartographic record of the process of rebuilding and remodelling. Lists of farm buildings are also recorded in surveys and valuations. Valuations are particularly useful for they often reveal their state of repair and indicate work that needed to be done. Estate correspondence and land agents' reports fill in the details. On 22 January 1870, for instance, the agent of the Wolverhampton Grammar School estate at Rushock (Worcs.) informed the trustees that William Lett of New Farm wanted another cow shed. This was required, William Lett had told him, because several cows had died when calving because there had been nowhere to house them.[60]

Many of the improvements made cost a good deal of money and it is therefore not surprising to note the growing interest which landowners and farmers showed in insuring their property in this period. As a result, more fire insurance policies were taken out which, because they describe the premises (and goods and machinery) being insured, are a valuable source of evidence.[61] If goods and machinery were included in the policy, the places in which they were kept were specified. Moreover, the size of the outbuildings can be estimated from the references to the number of bays they contained. The materials used in the construction were usually noted down because this information was highly relevant to the insurer. The information, deposited in the Guildhall Library in London, is not easy to use, however, as there are no indexes and the policies were enrolled in ledgers in the order that they were received. They are well worth looking at, however, especially if one has an idea when certain buildings were erected. Moreover, once one finds a local example, others tend to appear, as a batch of policies sent by a particular agent were recorded.

For information on farm buildings in general various sources can be examined (though they will have material on estate property too). The tithe awards, for instance, note the range of outbuildings belonging to farms and the accompany maps indicate their lay-out and size. The same sort of material is given in sales catalogues which deal with small freeholds as well as large estates. Descriptions of buildings, often accompanied by a map, can be found in title deeds which survive in greater numbers from the nineteenth century. The records of the reformed land tax returns of 1910, especially the field books, also contain much of interest. The marked-up ordnance survey maps belonging to the income tax officers should be looked at too, as should other large-scale ordnance survey maps.

Summary

Many of the improvements made to farm tools and equipment were small-scale modifications to existing items and passed unnoticed into history. Local variations abounded, often the result of minor refinements made by village craftsmen such as blacksmiths, ploughwrights cartwrights and carpenters who adapted the implements to suit local conditions. Other developments like the Rotherham plough or Tull's seed drill are better known, either because they were widely publicized or because they were brought into general use. Sometimes, the records enable local historians to chart the course of technological advance in their communities, providing evidence of not only the sort of tools and equipment being used there but also the time when innovations were adopted. Unfortunately, there is often a time-lag between the introduction of a new piece of equipment and the first documentary reference to it. Nonetheless, the material should still be used, especially for comparative purposes, since data from all parts of the country is equally affected by this limitation. Thus, local historians can relate their findings to developments elsewhere, comparing what happened to their areas with the pattern of events both regionally and nationally.

Appendix 1

SURREY R.O. 578, VIEW OF FRANKPLEDGE, MANOR OF EPSOM (SURREY), 16 OCTOBER 6 EDWARD VI (1552)

(Reproduced by kind permission of the Surrey R.O.)

N.B. Names in brackets are deleted in the text.
★ = pecator

Richard Kyng and William Osyver, tithingmen, present that they have given to the king for head-silver to this day, 6s. 8d.

Constable
Robert Bybye and Thomas Cawsten, jurors, present that the said Thomas Withdrew from the court and is in contempt, pain 3s. 4d.

Strays
None

Aletaster
Walter Hyde, juror, presents that all is well

Names of the jury for the king
John Helhous, (Robert Hewett), John Woodstock, William West, Oliver Parkehurst, James Bourne, (Geoffrey Lambard), John Woodman, Richard Kyng★, Thomas Cawsten★, John Tegge *alias* Pottelwood★, Robert Bybye★, (Thomas Tyllye★), William Ellyott, Richard Roger, (John Roger), (Henry Roger), (William Osyver★), (Robert Herde), (William Elys), (William Melsham), Thomas Asheted, (George Wylkyn), Geoffrey Marten, (Henry Chapman), Thomas Rychebell

The jury present that the lord of the manor must make good the gates called Hawell gates and Smyth Hatch and the gate to the church called the Church Hatch

John Wodstok and William West must make good the two stiles in Tam Lane as they are accustomed to before the next court, pain for each 3s. 4d.

Oliver Shyld to make a ditch lying at Redyngs Ditch, pain 4d.

Robert Bybye to scour his water course lying at the Cley between the house called the Tyle House and the Hooke before Lady Day, pain 4d.

John Hehous and Richard Roger from henceforth not to frequent a certain road with their plough and team, pain. 6s. 8d.

Essoins

John Mynne, John Payne (John Mynne gent., Edward Marland, Henry Mynne, Thomas Ellyott, John Rykman, John ›   ‹)

Homage

Robert Hewett, William Yeles, William Melsham, Elizabeth Mychell widow, William Osyver, Thomas Asshested, John ›   ‹, (Thomas Smyth), Oliver Parkehurst, Thomas Cawsten, John Wodstok, (James Potelwod), Geoffrey Lambert, Thomas Rychebell, Henry Chapman★, Robert Byby, John Helhowes, Rosa Wylkyn widow, John Wodman, Richard Rogers, Thomas Frank, Thomas Tylly, George Wylkyns, John Roger, James Burne★, Geoffrey Marten, (Edward Marten), Robert Herd, Richard Bray, Robert Broke, (Anna Rogers widow), (James Morley), Thomas Papworth, (Henry Rogers)

The homage say on their oath that John Mynne, Johanna Lady St. John, William Sawnder esquire, Richard Myles, Thomas Frank, Reginald Wylkyn (4d.), Edward Marlond (4d.), Thomas Ellyott (4d.), John Rykman (4d.), John Payne (8d.), George Wylkyn, William Kyng, Richard Roger, John Helhows owe suit of court and are in default

It is ordered by the homage that no-one shall common with their sheep in the common field from Lady Day to Michaelmas except on the down between the hedge there called Cookes Hedge and the king's way called the Dorking Way.

No-one having common in the common field shall remove the grain of others there, pain 20s.

To this court came Thomas Papworth and surrendered (property) that had been Thomas Ewell's and one and a half

acres of land lying at Harborow, one messuage with one croft
and half a virgate of land lying at the Cley with a messuage and
a half virgate formerly Maryottes Fayreharres (Robert Hewett
crossed out) with three acres of land lying at Foxholl to the use
of William Roydon, his heirs and assigns. To hold at the will
of the lord according to the customs of the manor, rendering
all due services and accidents and a heriot and an entry fine to
the lord upon admission.

John Basemore, son and heir of ›   ‹ Basemore deceased,
plaintiff, versus Oliver Parkehurst in a suit concerning land,
viz. one messuage with appurtenances called Horsted and of
›   ‹ acres called Rawntrew and of ›   ‹ acres of pasture
called Warren in Epsom.

Pannage of pigs
William Melsham (2d.), William Cheseman (3d.), James
Bygnall (4d.), Edward Hunt (4d.), John Richardson (2d.),
John Gully (2d.), Edward Jakes (1d.), Thomas Tayllour
(7½d.), John Frauncis (3d.), Thomas Durrant (1d.) Robert
Gully (1d.), Richard Wood (3d.), George Sutton (4d.),
William Tremayne (3d.), (James Godhelp 2d.), (Richard
Bykerstaff 1d.), John Helhous (4d.), Wiliam Ellyott (4d.),
Richard Ellyott (4d.), William West (4d.), John Woodman
(4d.), Agnes Hall widow (4d.), Richard Kyng (4d.), Geoffrey
Marten (4d.), Thomas Rychebell (4d.), Oliver Parkehurst
(4d.), John Woodstock ›   ‹, John Hemmawey (4d.),
Thomas Myller (6d.), George Sterre (6d.), Robert at lee (2d.),
Thomas Roger (4d.), Thomas Downe (2d.), Isabel Wadbroke
(1d.), Christiana Downe widow (2d.), Thomas Marsshe
(3d.), Walter Elys (3d.), Edward Seymond (1½d), John
Farrant (3d.), Thomas Geldam (1d.), Roger Goffe (2d.),
Lawrence Godfrey (2d.), William Cutler (3d.), (Thomas
Sutton 4d.), Thomas Cawsten (3d.), Richard Oxcombe (1d.),
John Romsey (1d.), Arnold Whyte (1d.), Richard Harryson
(2d.), John Byrd junior (2d.), John Bolter (3d.), Thomas
Mathewe (13d.), Richard Tybberd (1d.), William Osyver
junior (2d.)

SHROPS. R.O., 2028/BO/1/5/8, CUSTOM OF THE MANOR OF WORFIELD (SHROPS.) 1602

(The homage) there presents

That the fine for euery yeard land for admittance is 20ˢ for euery half yeard land 10ˢ and euery nooke land 5ˢ, and vnrated land is arbitrarie.

That Copiehold lands may not bee demised aboue three yeares without licence.

That euery Copieholder dieing seised of any Copiehold message or toft ought to pay herriots, viz for euery message one herriot, & euery toft one herriot, and euery Freeholder the like vnlesse such Freeholder can discharge it by his deeds

That a Copieholder may surrender his Copiehold lands, into the lords owne hands out of the Mannor or into two Customarie tenants hands or more out of the mannor, or into the Stewards hands w(i)thin the mannor to the vse of any others in fee simple, or fee taile, life liues or yeares, But then such surrender is to bee brought in within one yeare & a day, or else to be voide.

That the Copiehold lands descend to the eldest heire male if there be any or else (in default of heir male) to the eldest heir female, except the same copihold lands be otherwise surrendered

That after a surrender passed or Copieholder deceased the surrendre or heire, ought to come and desire to be admitted, within one yeare and a day, after such surrender or p(re)sentment of decease, or else the lord may sease the Copiehold lands, and take the p(ro)fitts thereof vntill such parties shall come into Court and desire to be admitted.

That if any Copieholder committ Treason or felonie his Copiehold lands in w(hi)ch he stands seiz(e)d in fee ought to escheat to the lord.

That noe p(er)son ought to sell cutt or carrie away, any of the lords woods vpon the waste or else where without license.

That euery Copieholder inhabiting w(i)thin his L(or)d-

(shi)pp, ought sokenedge to the lords myles, and the Townes of Kingslowe Stanlowe Chesterton Hilton Roughton (except two yeard land) Rowley Bradney Yewke Astrell & the Sond ought to all dawbe & thache Worfeild Mylle, and the Towneships of Hoccom Barnsley Swancott, the ocupiers of two yeard land in Roughton now W(illia)m Brookes, Burcott and Burcott Bromley Rindelford Alscott Winscott Newton and Stableford, ought to wall dawbe and thache Rindelford mylle, vpon notice giuen, as oft as need shall require, respectiuely in p(ar)ts as heretofore.

That euery yeard land within this Lordship of copiehold land payeth vi^s viii^d cheife rent, except fower yeard in Hollon wich payeth viii^s, for euery yeard land except two halfe yeard lands in the Sond in tenures of Roger Rowley Gent & Rich Sond, and all ratet land to the same p(ro)porc(i)on

There is yearly alowed out of the lords meddow two doles p(ar)cell of the same meddow to the vicar called the vicares doles onely for the Tythe hay one dole called the Reiue Rick dole to the lords Reiue, and one dole called the hurst, and nine foot round about the meddow called the stafe to the lords Biddle

That the Copieholders (except Hollon) ought and doe yearly mowe make into hay the grasse yearely growing in the lords meddowe vpon reasonable summons in the Church for w(hi)ch the lord or his tenant of the same alloweth yearely 16^d

That the lord of Hollon ought yearely to finde the lords Biddle, who ought yearly to gather the fines, heriots, and amerciaments, and pay ouer the same, and the Biddle may distraine for all p(er)quisits of court

That the homage ought yearly to choose a Reiue, who ought yearly to gather the lords rent, and the Biddle and Reiue are to see the lords grasse in the said lords meddow mowed and made

That if A Copieholder surrender any copiehold lands into Customarie tenants hands, and die before such surrender be passed and brought into Co(u)rt, yet those custom(arie) tena(u)nts may at any Court within one yeare and a day after such passing of the same into their hands surr(ender) the same into the lords hands as attorneys or state bearers, though the same be after the decease of the surrender But in this case the lord shall haue his herriot if the same be herriotable, for that it was not p(re)sented or surrendred in the lords Court in the life of the surrenderer.

That if any Copieholder die seased in fee, of any Copiehold lands or tenements w(i)thin this mannor having a wife then liuing, then that wife shall hold the same customarie tenements during her life by the custom of the said mannor.

That a man and his wife, where the wif hath any customarie estate w(i)thin this mannor, may by two customarie tenants or more as their Attorneys surrender any such Customarie tenements, but such surrender shall not barr the wife except shee come and be exam(ined) by the steward w(i)thin the mannor, and how she & all claiming for(?) her shall bee barred for euer

But the custom is(?) that neither man or woman estates of any estate in tayle, may surrender or alien any such lands longer then for their liues, but such tenants or tenants in tayle may surr(ender) their Customarie tenements to the vse of his heir or their heir apparent in fee, And that surrender is a discontinuance of the intayle, And then such heir apparent may surrender & alien the same at pleasure, or if the tenant in tayle die, the heir of such tenant in tayle, may desire to bee admitted in fee, and such admittance is and shall bee a discontinuance of such estate tayle

The Reiue and Biddle respectiuely ought to yeald their accompts to the lord for the time being or his auditor or his debutie, that is to say the Biddle at Michal(mas), & the Reeve the rent dayes respectively.

Appendix 3

NOTTS. UNIV. LIB., MSS DEPT., Mi A34, SHEEP ACCOUNT 1553–4 OF THE WILLOUGHBYS OF WOLLATON (NOTTS.)

To Henry Avery the xiiiith of June for xxxvi Wasshers and casters of sheepe into the water and Landers at Wollaton	xii^s
To the miller for his water	?^{d}
for Ale for the Sheppardes and cariage of the flekes	ii^d
Item to the sayd Henry Avery for xxxvi wasshers & kesters into the water at Basfoord	xii^s
To the miller for his water	ii^d
Item in breadd and Ale	vi^d
Item for breadd flekes and Ale	i^d
Item for a mannes charg(e)s th(a)t went for the shepparde to warsoppe	vi^d
To Iveson for grease	vi^d
To him for his charg(e)s vntill sondaye at none	viii^d
To the shepparde of warsoppe for greace	iiii^d
To hymn for his charg(e) that brought the flece	i^d
Item for the sheppardes Charg(e)s	viii^d
Item to the shepparde of basforde for greace	iiii^d
Item for the Clyppars beddes and the Sheppardes	xviii^d
Item to ii women that gathered Lokes	iiii^d
Item to Will(ia)m Mericox, Raven & Roo for servinge the Clippers ii daies a pece	xvi^d
To the Clippers for shering of wollaton flock	xi^s
Item for a q(ua)rter of malt against the sheepe Clypping this yere	xviii^s
Item for vi strikes of rye	xviii^s
Item for white breadd	viii^d
Item for butter	xvii^d
Item for Chease	xx^d
Item for di(midio) roke of Coles and for the cariage	xvi^d
To Godbesere for dressing the meate	xii^d

Item for bar . . .   iiii^d

Sum(ma) Pagine(m) iiii^{li} v^s ii^d

To Parkes and brownesworde for winding the wolle		xi^s
for brow(n)swordes boorde at Henleis the space ofii^s viii daies		vi^d
To a woman that served hym		xvii^d
To the shepparde of warsoppe xxvis Julii for his q(uarte)rs wag(e)s due at Lammas		x^s
To Henry Avery for his q(uarte)rs wag(e)s		xv^s
To Avery for his Lyvery then due		x^s
To Iveson for his q(uarte)rs wag(e)s		x^s
To Hughe Irelande for his wag(e)s		x^s
To ii at Radfoorde for a daye mowinge at Arnaide closse		xx^d
To Iveson for mowing of the reste & making of it &iiii^s stacking of the same		viii^d
To Iveson for his rent at Arnalde – iii^s iiii^d – and for hedging the closse for the shepe and making of a gate – ii^s	v^s	iiii^d
Item to Dennis Backster of warsoppe the v^c daye of October by the commandm(en)t of Mr berwick and John Hall at hunters at Nott(ingham) for iii yeres rent of a closse to come after Candlemas next as by a bill appereth		xxi^s
To Hughe Ireland for his q(uarte)rs wag(e)s due at Martillmas		x^s
To the shepparde of warsoppe for his wag(e)s		x^s
To Iveson for his Lyvery	vi^s	viii^d
To hym for his wag(e)s		x^s
To Irelande for his lyvery	vi^s	viii^d
To the shepparde of basfoord for his Lyvery	vi^s	viii^d
To the shepparde of warsoppe for the taxe of the shepe there		xxii^d

Sum(ma) pag(inem) vii^{li} xiiii^s vii^d

For mowing of the Closse at warsoppe and mynglyng of the same		xviii^d
Item to hym for cariage of the tythe wolle		iiii^d
To Henry Avery for his wag(e)s due at Martillmas	xv^s	

To hym for branding the flockes at Arnolde and   xvi^d
basfoorde

Item for branding at Wollatton   xii^d

To Avery for the cariage of iiii Lodes of haye to   viii^d
Basfoorde   iiii^s

To Avery for his q(uarte)rs wag(e)s due at Candell-
mas   xv^s

To Irelande for his q(uarte)rs wag(e)s   x^s

To Iveson for his q(uarte)rs wag(e)s   x^s

To the Shepparde of warsoppe for his q(uarte)rs
wagis then due   x^s

To Mr Medeley for the rent of the shepe groundes at
Lenton due at Michaellmas for one hole yere then
ended in annis
regno(rum) phi(lippi) reg(i)s et marie Regine 2° et 3° vii^{li} xii^s

To Henry Avery for marking the flock at Warsopp   xxi^d

Item for pitche that he bought   viii^{dob}

To hym for greace   xvi^d

Item for the rent of the sheepe grounde at Arnalde   xii^s
due at Michaellmas 2° et 3°

Sum(ma) pagine(m) xi^{li} xi^s vii^d ob

VALUATION OF THE WOLVERHAMPTON GRAMMAR SCHOOL ESTATE AT RUSHOCK (WORCS.), SEPTEMBER 1841 (W. G. S. ARCHIVES)

The New Farm: Joseph Lett, tenant

No. on Plan	Description	State	Quantity a.r.p.	Price per Acre	Annual Value
193	March Field	Ara	7.0.22	20s.	10.14.01
194	Rushbridge Meadow	Past	5.1.24	25s.	9.11.02
195	Road		1.00		
196	March Field Closes	Ara	4.1.29	32s.	7.01.09
197	Oak Tree Piece	Ara	13.2.25	32s.	21.17.00
198	Stepstone Meadow	Past	3.3.01	30s.	5.12.08
203	Cutnell and Newland	Ara	12.0.05	32s.	19.05.00
204	South Sinderlands	Ara	16.3.24	32s.	11.00.09
205	Little Hardidge	Ara	16.1.17	32s.	26.03.04
207	Meadow	Past	10.0.00	22s.	11.00.00
208	March Field Butts	Ara	2.2.28	32s.	4.05.07
210	Six Lands	Past	2.0.21	30s.	3.03.11
214	North Sinderlands	Ara	7.1.02	30s.	10.17.10
216	Callimore Meadow	Past	3.29	32s.	1.07.11
217	Callimore	Ara	8.3.23	28s.	12.09.00
220	Bradford Hill	Ara	4.1.11	30s.	6.09.06
221	Meadow	Past	3.0.19	30s.	4.13.06
223	Radnall	Ara	8.3.38	28s.	12.04.07
224	Dean Close	Ara	4.2.01	32s.	7.04.02
225	New Meadow	Past	2.3.13	32s.	14.10.07
226	Brook Acre	Ara	5.0.24	32s.	8.04.09
227	The Deans	Ara	7.0.31	32s.	11.10.02
228	Four Acres	Ara	7.0.33	32s.	11.10.07
229	Mill Field Tyning	Ara	6.1.25	30s.	9.12.02
230	Brookside Meadow	Past	6.0.30	30s.	9.05.07
231	Swan Pool	Ara	9.2.17	30s.	14.08.02

232	Mill Field	Ara	13.2.25	30s.	20.09.08
233	The Sling	Past	14.0.13	34s.	23.18.09
234	The New House, Out-buildings, Yard &c		2.1.35		15.00.00
235	Aston	Ara	5.3.30	30s.	8.18.01
236	Quarry Aston	Ara	6.1.10	28s.	8.16.00
237	Well Furlong	Ara	5.0.36	30s.	7.16.09
238	Well Meadow	Past	2.0.12	40s.	4.03.00
240	Wall Close	Ara	1.0.07	35s.	1.16.06
248	Big Meadow	Past	3.3.25	40s.	7.16.03
256	Round Pool	Past	12.1.33	36s.	22.08.05

Observations

The general repairs of this Farm are but trifling and will be effected for about £30.

The Front of the House has given way and will at a future time require a considerable expenditure but upon examination I am led to the belief that it may continue in its present state for some years longer.

The farm buildings are inconveniently arranged the Cart Stable and Old Barn should be taken down and re-built in a different position, with the addition of another Carthouse; this alteration would so far add to the convenience of the occupation as to justify an increased rental of £6 per Cent on an expenditure of £350.

The present Value of the Farm is £385

Appendix 5

SHROPS. R.O. 1267/39, COUNTERPART LEASE OF A FARM AT COSFORD (SHROPS.) BY JOHN JONES OF RUCKLEY GRANGE, ESQUIRE, TO ELIZABETH EARP OF COSFORD, WIDOW, AND WILLIAM EARP OF COSFORD, FARMER.

Abstract of Schedule

Fields and buildings individually listed, together with acreages.
In Parish of Donnington: 282a.0r.17p.
In Parish of Albrighton: 180a.0r.11p.

Covenants

Counterpart agreement to let a farm with mansion house, cottages and buildings at Cosford in the parishes of Donington and Albrighton, late in the occupation of Mr. William Earp, now Elizabeth Earp.

Timber and minerals reserved and the exclusive right to all sport.

Rent £922. A further £20 for every acre of land in certain specified fields broken up or sown with hemp, flax or rape or mown twice in a year for hay or fodder. Tenant to pay all taxes except land tax, tithe rent charge and landlord's property tax.

Covenant for repair, the tenant being allowed timber in the rough, bricks, tiles and lime at the kilns.

The lands are to be managed in husbandlike manner, the gutters and watercourses scoured at least once a year.

All hay, clover, fodder, straw, dung, compost and manure used on the farm or left at the end of the term, and one-third of the corn sown on a fallow and one-half of that corn sown on a brush, with the tithe of it, to be left for Jones without compensation.

The following course of tillage is to be used: the first year, winter corn; the second year, the land to be fallowed and sown with turnips to be eaten on premises; the third year, the land to be sown with barley and at the same time laid down with a sufficient quantity of the best clover and rye grass seed and not to be broken up again before the second Michaelmas seedness at soonest after; the ground to be well manured.

At the Michaelmas seedness preceeding the determination of this agreement, no more than 105 acres shall be sown with winter corn and that upon clean clover leys of the first or second years growth or upon lands well summer fallowed, and not after turnips or other crops.

On 1st. November the tenant shall hay up all the clover and on 1st. January after the meadow and pasture land and shall not graze them. The succeeding tenant is to be permitted to enter at any time after 1st. November preceeding the determination of the lease.

The tenant agrees to preserve the quicksetts and timber trees and preserve the game.

During the term 70 waggon loads of well-burnt clod lime or other manure as approved by Jones, are to be purchased and drawn to the farm and spread.

The tenant is to perform four days' carriage for Jones as required, for carriage of coal or as he shall think fit.

Jones agrees that after the expiration of the term, the tenants shall have room in part of the outbuildings and folds and a convenient piece of land for threshing out her corn and grain, tying up her cattle and spending her hay and fodder on the premises until 1st. May next, with liberty of fencing and cotting all winter corn as she shall have sown and liberty of stacking it in the rickyard and threshing it in the barn until 1st. May next after the harvest, provided she leave the whole of the straw and chaff and one-third of the corn sown on a fallow and one-half of the corn sown on a brush, with the tithe, for the benefit of Jones.

Jones shall pay her for the clover sown at the spring seedness next preceding the determination of the agreement the price it cost in the market when bought, provided the lands have been properly hayed up.

The tenant has the right to take rabbits with ferrets between 1st. November and 1st. March each year.

She is to be paid £10 *per annum* for trespass to, from and at the stone quarries.

The agreement is for one year and from year to year, determinable at the end of any year at six months' notice.

Signatures of Elizabeth Earp, William Earp.
Witness: Charles Spence of Tong, Shifnal

LICHFIELD JOINT R.O., B/V/6, GLEBE TERRIER OF KINNERSLEY UPON THE WEALD MOORS, 1612

(Reproduced by kind permission of the Lichfield Diocesan Registrar)

Imprimis the Dwellinge house or p(ar)sonage contayninge contayninge two bayes of buildinge beinge thatched with strawe and havinge two fier places.

Item the kitchen contayninge two bayes of buildinge with a kilne.

Item the barne beinge three bayes of buildinge with a stable at the end thereof And a carthouse.

Item other houses for cattle aboute three bayes of buildinge.

Item a garden and orchard about halfe an acre of land.

Seuerall glebe

Two little closes the one adioyninge to the bull peece on the south p(ar)te and to Westons peece on the East p(ar)te and the com(m)on feild on the other p(ar)te contayninge halfe an acre of land. The other at the Rodway adioyninge to the gale and the Rodway beinge aboute an acre.

Item Foure beast(e)s grasse in a pasture called the gale.

There is noe other seu(er)all pasture or meadowe ground belonginge to the p(ar)sonage but such as lately was inclosed and taken out of the com(m)on moore for w(hi)ch there is rent payd by the p(ar)son to the lord of the mannour All which ground(e)s the lord of the mannor or the freehoulders may at there pleasure cast open or make com(m)on as it was before.

Feild lande

Rodway Feild

Impr(imi)s One land shootynge vpon Jewes style beinge about halfe an acre of land

Item three butt(e)s shootynge vpon the Rodway beinge about an acre

Item one little smale butt ore the Rodway hades

Item two butt(e)s and a pyke neere to Gravenors gale edge beinge about an acre

Item three butt(e)s nere Haway hedge beinge aboute an acre

Item one litle butt at the gravell pytt

Item Foure butt(e)s shootynge vpon the way to Sydnall at Ewes horne corner at the end of the vtmost is a hadland at the vpper end of the longest butt are three other butt(e)s all these are in quantity aboute twoo acres.

Sydnay Feild

Impr(imi)s at the were furlonge two butt(e)s beinge aboute halfe an acre

Item two little butt(e)s neere the gospell greave beinge aboute halfe an acre

Item one butt on this syde the gospell greve shootynge on the land of Thoms Harp(er) beinge aboute a quarter of an acre

Item one butt and two Pykes lyinge on ether syde a pitt by the foote way leadinge to the lord(e)s Doale neare the gospell greave beinge aboute halfe an acre

Item two butt(e)s vpon the over branton furlonge neere to the eller greave beinge three quarters of an acre

Item sixe butt(e)s vpon Bradway furlonge beinge aboute ii acres

Item foure butt(e)s more neere to the same place aboute an acre

Item sixe little butt(e)s lyinge betwixt Jo(h)n Bells furlonge on the one p(ar)te and Margaret Westons on thoth(er) p(ar)te beinge aboute an acre and a halfe

The Hill Feild

Impr(imi)s at the head of the furlonge shootynge vpon Haway hedge foure butt(e)s whereof one is a hadland beinge aboute an acre

Item fyve butt(e)s lyinge vpon the same hadland beinge aboute two acres

Item three butt(e)s vpon the fearney furlonge eache butt standinge vpon it selfe beinge aboute an acre

Item one land at Walborne shootynge vpon the wall ground

Item one land vpon the hill aboute halfe an acre

Item three land(e)s and three pykes at hawmoore flat aboute an acre

Item two butt(e)s in whittingham his crofte by buttery way
aboute half an acre

Theie are in the p(ar)ishe of Kynn(er)sley onely Twelue
tenement(e)s or plowland(e)s there is neith(er) gentleman
yeoman nor freeholder w(i)thin the p(ar)ishe. the p(ar)son
hath two Oxen and two mares wherew(i)th he soweth his land
and carried his corne and hay.

The tenthes due to the Kinges Ma(jes)tie for the Rectory
aforesaid is – xii^s ii^d

W(i)ll(iam) Bailye Rector ib(ide)m
John Gravenor) ⎫
Robart whittingham) ⎬ Churchwardens
                    ⎭
Thomas Harp(er)
John Bell
Thomas Baker
John Symonds

Appendix 7

CONTRASTING FARMING SYSTEMS ILLUSTRATED IN THE TITHE FILES

a) P.R.O. (Kew), IR 18/10090, Tithe File of Barnes (Surrey), 1837

Description

The Parish of Barnes is situated on the Banks of the Thames about six miles from London in a bend of the River which nearly surrounds it on three sides–it is very level and for the most part good land varying from sandy loam to gravel, with some good pastures and a considerable proportion of sound and healthy Thames Meadows besides several richly fruited gardens some of which are walled.

Rent Charge an increase

. . . The common mode of estimating the value of agricultural crops is not applicable to the Parish of Barnes where the cultivation of corn is rather the Exception than the rule of husbandry; where garden produce of every variety occupies a considerable portion of the cultivated ground, and even the green crops in the arable district are grown for the purpose of distant sale instead of the sustenance of the cattle of the Occupiers–to give anything like an accurate statement of the succession of crops stimulated by constant manure, and varied according to the fluctuations in the demand for them in the market would be impracticable and extremely fallacious I have not therefore attempted it.

b) P.R.O. (Kew), IR 18/9059, Tithe File of Longstock (Hants.), 1840

Description

This parish, running a great length close up to the northern side of Stockbridge, forms a tract of light calcarious loam of very poor quality, much of it totally unfit for the growth of wheat.

The Water Meadows are mostly very coarse, lying on a

peat, & abounding in rushes. The Downs are good, & the herbage, although not heavy, is very sweet. There are no titheable Underwoods. The parish is well farmed, & the quantity of produce considerably increased of late years by a spirited attention to sheep farming. Very little sainfoin is grown, the Water Meadows chiefly supplying the sheep with hay.

EXTRACT FROM THE TOLL BOOK OF ST THOMAS'S DAY FAIR, HELD AT TAUNTON ON 7 JULY 1629 (SOMERSET R.O., DD/SP 341)

Easter Budell de Holway Wester Budell de Holway	Jur(ors) at Blackwater
Budell de Pondisford Budell de Cofffe	Jur(ors) at Frisehill
Budell de Staplegrove Budell de Naylesborne	Jur(ors) at Tonebridge
Budell de Hull Jur(or) at Back Lane	

page 3 *verso*

4 John Pearce of Baddleton sold vnto John Derham of north curry ii steeres price viii^{li}

4 Samuell Dyer of norton butcher sold vnto John Stone of Vsculme in Com(itatu) Devon i bay nagg with ob' ›*obolus*halfpenny mark‹ vnder the farther eare price xxx^{s} p(er) vowcher Nicho(las) Hurtnold of Bradford

4 Hughe Farr of Hinington Drifler exchanged with John Stone of Ashbrittle i grey nagge with spade marke in the neere eare & LH in the neere buttocke for i bay mare with ob' in the neere eare

4 John Washer of Fityhead in Com(itatu) Som(er)sety sold vnto Robert Meade of Street ii steeres i Red sparked & i swarte steere price ix^{li}

4 John Babbe of Chellerswood sold vnto William Saffen of Bicknoller i steere price iiii^{li}

2 Agnes Browne of Enmore vid(ow) sold vnto John Maun dry of Haberton i Dicker of lether price vii^{li} xv^{s}

3 John Frye of Ashbrittle in Com(itatu) Som(er)sety sold vnto Nicho(las) Cornelius of Cudworth in the s(ai)d county i bay mare with ob' vnder the neere eare price iii^{li} viii^{s} iiii^{d} p(er) vowcher nicholas Barbor of Combestoke

4 William Spreat of milverton sold vnto William Clarke of Huishe ii oxen viii^{li} xii^{d}

4   (omission) sold vnto Mr Turker of Ilmister ii heafers

4   John Fursey of wellington sold vnto John Bowden of Dolishe i steere wanded price – iiii^{li} x^s

3   John Tuthill of Walles in Com(itatu) Glamorgan sold vnto Thomas Sealye of Creech 80 sheepe price xxv^{li} vi^s viii^d

2   Simon Palfrye of Milverton sold vnto John Lokier i Dicker of leather price viii^{li} x^s

2   John Beadon of Stogumber sold vnto John Lokier i Dicker of lether price viii^{li} x^s

2   Thomas Symons of Stogurssey sold vnto Alex Sheeres of Stogursey i Dicker of lether price v^{li} x^s

    Robert nation of Kingston sold vnto John Glanfeild of Hinington ii Dicker of lether price xvi^{li} vi^s viii^d

    John Bryant of lidyard Epi(scopi) sold vnto John Glanfeild halfe a dicker of lether price iii^{li} xiii^s iiii^d

REFERENCES

Introduction (pp. 11–16)

1. See the books listed under Further Reading, p.215
2. U. Lambert, *Blechingley: A Short History* (Surrey Arch. Soc., Guildford 1949)

Chapter One (pp. 19–31)

1. E. Miller & J. Hatcher, *Medieval England* (Longman, London, 1978) (hereafter Miller & Hatcher), p. 7
2. P. D. A. Harvey, *Manorial Records*, Archives and the User, no. 5 (British Records Assoc., 1984), pp. 16–17
3. J. B. Harley, 'The Hundred Rolls of 1279', *The Amateur Historian*, 5 (1), 1961, pp. 9–18
4. Harvey, *op. cit.*, pp. 19–23
5. H. S. A. Fox, 'The Chronology of Enclosure and Economic Development in Medieval Devon', *Econ. Hist. Review*, 2nd. ser., 28 (2) 1975, p. 185
6. M. W. Beresford, *The Lost Villages of England* (Lutterworth Press, London, 1954), p. 427, f.n.32
7. A. R. H. Baker, 'Evidence in the "Nonarum Inquisitiones" of Contracting Arable in England during the Early Fourteenth Century', in A. R. H. Baker, J. D. Hamshere & J. Langton, eds. *Geographical Interpretation of Historical Sources*, (David & Charles, Newton Abbot, 1970), p. 86
8. C. Dyer, *Lords and Peasants in a Changing Society* (Cambridge U.P., 1980), p. 68
9. This section is based upon Harvey, *op. cit.*, pp. 25–41
10. B. M. S. Campbell, 'Agricultural Progress in Medieval England: Some Evidence form Eastern Norfolk', *Econ. Hist. Review*, 2nd. ser., 36 (1), 1983, pp. 26–44
11. H. S. A. Fox, The Alleged Transformation from Two-Field to Three-field Systems in Medieval England, *Econ. Hist. Review*, 39 (4), 1986, pp. 526–48
12. Miller & Hatcher, p. 217

13. Harvey, *op. cit.*, p. 22.
14. M. Hollings, ed., 'The Red Book of Worcester, i–ii', *Worcs. Hist. Soc.* (1934), pp. 65, 72, 77–9, 81
15. Dyer, *op. cit.*, p. 321
16. W. J. Blair, ed., 'The Early Manorial Records of Leatherhead', *Procs. of the Leatherhead & District History Society*, 4 (1), 1977, pp. 12–18
17. Dyer, *op. cit.*, p. 321
18. J. West, *Village Records* (Macmillan, London, 1962), p. 35
19. H. P. R. Finberg, 'Anglo-Saxon England to 1042', in H. P. R. Finberg, ed., *The Agrarian History of England and Wales, I.ii, A.D. 43–1042* (Cambridge U.P., 1972), p. 496
20. A. A. Dibben, *Title Deeds, 13th. to 19th. Centuries*, H72, (The Historical Assoc., London, 1968), p. 18
21. F. G. Emmison, Final Concords, *The Local Historian*, 14 (7), 1981, pp. 411–16
22. J. Langdon, *Horses, Oxen and Technological Innovation* (Cambridge U.P., 1986), pp. 179–80
23. A. R. H. Baker, *op. cit.*, p. 85
24. R. J. P. Kain & H. C. Prince, *The Tithe Surveys of England and Wales* (Cambridge U.P., 1985), pp. 7–10
25. R. H. Hilton, *The Economic Development of Some Leicestershire Estates* (Oxford U.P., 1947), pp. 63–5
26. Dyer, *op. cit.*, p. 329

Chapter Two (pp. 32–47)

1. J. Thirsk, 'Agricultural Policy: Public Debate and Legislation', in J. Thirsk, ed., *The Agrarian History of England and Wales, V, 1640–1750*, (Cambridge U.P., 1985) (hereafter *Agrarian History V*), ii, pp. 329–34, 346–56
2. See, for instance, A. C. Edwards, ed., *The Account Books of Benjamin Mildmay, Earl Fitzwalter* (Regency Press, London, 1977), p. xi, for comment on Earl Fitzwalter's method of accounting
3. M. E. Finch, 'Five Northants Families', 1540–1640, *Northants Record Society*, 1956, p. 193; Peter Edwards, *The Horse Trade of Tudor and Stuart England* (Cambridge U.P., 1988), pp. 149–53
4. Warwicks, R. O., Warwick Castle Colln. CR 1886/412, abstract of accounts by Francis Parker, auditor
5. Peter Edwards, 'Farming in a North Worcestershire Parish: Rushock 1572–1972', unpub. M.A. dissertation, Leicester University, 1973 (hereafter Rushock), p. 31

6. Rushock, pp. 84–6
7. H. King & A. Harris, eds., 'A Survey of the Manor of Settrington', *Yorks. Arch. Soc.*, Record Series, 126, 1960, p. x
8. Ibid., Tables 1–6, at the end of the book
9. Herefs. & Worcs. R.O. (Hereford) Glebe Terriers, 10/30, Stanton Lacy, 8 June 1607
10. Shrops. R.O. 167–51, Wem 29 June 1561
11. Staffs. R.O., Bradford Colln., D1287/18/15
12. A. C. Chibnall, *Fiefs and Fields of a Buckinghamshire Village* (Cambridge U.P., 1965), pp. 286–9
13. J. R. W. Whitfield, 'The Enclosure Movement in North Shropshire', *Trans. Caradoc & Severn Valley Soc.*, 11, 1939, p. 55; P.R.O. C3/200/90; Staffs. R.O., Sutherland Colln D593/2/1/7; PRO, E134 10 James I, Mich. 4
14. E. Melling, ed., *Kentish Sources III: Aspects of Agriculture and Industry* (Kent County Council, Maidstone, 1961), pp. 32–59
15. L. Toulmin Smith, ed., *Leland's Itinerary in England and Wales* (Centaur Press, Fontwell, 1964), V, pp. 155–6
16. Ibid., IV, p. 19
17. C. Morris, ed., *The Journeys of Celia Fiennes* (The Cresset Press, London, 1947), p. 177
18. P. R. Edwards, The Development of Dairy Farming on the North Shropshire Plain in the Seventeenth Century, *Midland Hist.*, 3–4, 1978, pp. 175–90
19. W. G. Hoskins, *The Midland Peasant* (Macmillan, London, 1965), pp. 154–6
20. P. Glennie, 'Continuity and Change in Hertfordshire Agriculture 1550–1700: II – Trends in Crop Yields and their Determinants', *Agric. Hist. Review*, 36 (2), 1988, pp. 145–61
21. P. Riden, *Local History: A Handbook for Beginners* (Batsford, London, 1983), pp. 62–4
22. PRO, PROB 4/1675
23. Lichfield Joint R.O., Probate Inventory of Richard Rowley of Wyken (Worfield) 7 june 1605 (no date of probate)
24. Herefs. & Worcs. R.O. (Worcester), B.A. 3585, Class 008.7/1593/124
25. Herefs. & Worcs. R.O. (Hereford), Probate Will 1546/17, Thomas Addams of Barrow

26. N. Evans, Tithe Books as a Source for the Local Historian', *The Local Historian*, 14 (1), 1980, p.25
27. E. J. Evans, *The Contentious Tithe* (R.K.P., London, 1976), pp. 50–8
28. E. J. Evans, Tithing Customs and Disputes: The Evidence of Glebe Terriers, 1698–1850, *Agric. Hist. Review*, 18 (1), 1970, pp. 17–35
29. Ibid, p. 25
30. J. J. Bagley, *Historical Interpretations I: Sources of Medieval History 1066–1540* (David & Charles, Newton Abbot, 1965), p. 248
31. Shrops. R.O., Adderley Estate (Corbett) 327/140
32. F. Milton, *The English Magistracy* (Oxford U.P., 1967), pp. 8–13
33. Lincs. Archive Office, Horbling Parish Records 7/1, 7/3, 12/2
34. Edwards, *Horse Trade*, pp. 8–9
35. M. W. Beresford, 'The Poll Tax and Census of Sheep, 1549', *Agric. Hist. Review*, 2, 1954, pp. 22–4
36. Ibid., pp. 26–7
37. Ibid., p. 24

Chapter Three (pp. 48–65)

1. J. D. Chambers & G. E. Mingay, *The Agricultural Revolution 1750–1880* (Batsford, London, 1966) (hereafter Chambers & Mingay), pp. 123–6, 148–9, 156–7
2. J. Thirsk, *English Peasant Farming: The Agrarian History of Lincolnshire from Tudor to Recent Times* (R.K.P., London, 1957), p. 197
3. Chambers & Mingay, p. 170
4. R. A. C. Parker, *Coke of Holkham: A Financial and Agricultural Study 1707–1842* (Clarendon Press, Oxford, 1975), pp. 119–20
5. M. A. Havinden, *Estate Villages: A Study of the Berkshire Villages of Ardington and Lockinge* (Lund Humphries, London, 1966), pp. 91, 124
6. Wolverhampton G.S. Archives, Mr Matthews's Report, March 1844
7. Havinden, *op. cit.*, p. 76
8. R. J. Colyer, 'The Use of Estate Farm Accounts as Sources for Nineteenth Century Agricultural History,' *Local Historian*, 11 (7), 1975, p. 406

9. Celia Miller, *Rain and Ruin: The Diary of an Oxfordshire Farmer, John Simpson Calvertt 1875–1900* (Alan Sutton, Gloucester, 1983), *passim*

10. David Thomas, *Agriculture in Wales during the Napoleonic Wars* (Cardiff U.P., 1963), pp. 18–20

11. Ibid., pp. 20–1

12. D. G. Hey, 'The 1801 Crop Returns for South Yorkshire', *Yorks. Arch. Journal*, 42 (4), 1967–70, p. 464

13. M. Turner, 'Agricultural Productivity in England in the Eighteenth Century: Evidence from Crop Yields', *Econ. Hist. Review*, 2nd. ser., 35 (4), 1982, p. 497

14. PRO (Kew), H.O. 67/14/165

15. Thomas, *op. cit.*, pp. 21–3

16. Hey, *op. cit.*, p. 456

17. Ibid.

18. Ibid.

19. Chambers & Mingay, pp. 73–4

20. Quoted in F. Beavington, 'The Development of Market Gardening in Bedfordshire 1799–1939', *Agric. Hist. Review*, 23 (1), 1975, p. 25

21. D. Taylor, 'The English Dairy Industry, 1860–1930', *Econ. Hist. Review*, 2nd. ser., 29 (4), 1976, p. 587

22. J. M. Martin, 'The Social and Economic Origins of the Vale of Evesham Market Gardening Industry', *Agric. Hist. Review*, 33 (1), 1985, p. 43

23. Kain & Prince, *Tithe Surveys*, p. 62

24. Ibid., p. 62

25. Ibid., pp. 91–103

26. Ibid., p. 77

27. Ibid., p. 103–6

28. E. A. Cox & B. R. Dittmer, 'The Tithe Files of the Mid-Nineteenth Century', *Agric. Hist. Review*, 13 (1), 1965, pp. 2–9

29. Ibid., pp. 4–5

30. PRO (Kew), IR 18/10167, Tithe File of Mortlake, Surrey

31. Cox & Dittmer, *op. cit.*, pp. 3–4

32. Ibid., pp. 10–16

33. This section is based on J. P. Dodd, 'The Agricultural Statistics for 1854: An Assessment of their Value', *Agric. Hist. Review*, 35 (2), 1987, pp. 163–5

34. C. S. Orwin & E. H. Wheetham, *History of British Agriculture: 1846–1914* (David & Charles, Newton Abbot, 1971), p. 181

35. PRO, Leaflet 14, *Agricultural Statistics: Parish Summaries* MAF 68
36. Ibid.; J. T. Coppock, The Agricultural Returns as a Source for Local History', *The Amateur Historian*, 4 (2), 1958–9, pp. 49–55
37. PRO (Kew), MAF 68/143; MAF 68/2252
38. This section is based on B. Short & M. Reed, 'An Edwardian Land Source: The Finance (1909–10) Act 1910 Records', *Journal of Soc. of Archivists*, 8 (2), 1986, pp. 95–103
39. W. H. Peek, ed., *Extracts from the Court Rolls of the Manor of Wimbledon, extending from 1 Edward IV to A.D. 1864* (Wyman & Sons, London, 1866), *passim*
45. F. W. Cowe, Wimbledon Vestry Minutes, 1736, 1743–1788, *Surrey Record Society*, 25, 1964, *passim*; Bourne Hall, Ewell, Local History Dept., Vestry Book of Ewell
41. Orwin & Wheetham, *op. cit.*, p. 29
42. Ibid., p. 293
43. Flow chart compiled by Ms Ruth Bagley, Shropshire County Archivist. I am grateful to her for allowing me to publish it
44. P. E. Dewey, *British Agriculture in the First World War*, (R.K.P., London, 1989), pp. 171–96
45. J. Sheail, 'Land Improvement and Reclamation: The Experiences of the First World War in England and Wales', *Agric. Hist. Review*, 24 (2) 1976, pp. 111–12

Chapter Four (pp. 66–89)

1. The classic work on the English landscape is W. G. Hoskins's *The Making of The English Landscape* (Hodder & Stoughton, London, 1953). Though in places it has been superseded by the work of landscape historians such as Christopher Taylor, it is still the best book to read as an introduction to the subject
2. For the effect of population change on settlement and the landscape, read C. C. Taylor, *Village and Farmstead* (George Philip, London, 1983)
3. C. C. Taylor, *Fields in the English Landscape* (Alan Sutton, Gloucester, *passim*
4. W. G. Hoskins, *Fieldwork in Local History* (Faber & Faber, London, 1967)
5. M. D. Hooper, 'Hedges and Local History', in *Hedges and*

Local History (National Council of Social Service, London, 1971), pp. 6–13. The other articles in the booklet are also useful.

6. For instance, T. Hussey, 'Hedgerow History', *The Local Historian*, 17 (6), 1987, pp. 327–42

7. M. Reed, 'Anglo-Saxon Boundaries', in M. Reed, ed., *Discovering Past Landscapes* (Croom Helm, London, 1984), pp. 261–306. For an introduction to the subject read K. Bailey, 'Anglo-Saxon Charters and the Local Historian', *The Local Historian*, 17 (2), 1988, pp. 71–7

8. H. P. R. Finberg, 'Anglo-Saxon England', in Finberg, *Agrarian History, I.ii*, pp. 486–7

9. Also read H. C. Darby, ed., *A New Historical Geography of England before 1600* (Cambridge U.P., 1976), pp. 39–74

10. Ibid., pp. 52–7

11. Hoskins, *Fieldwork*, pp. 48–9

12. M. T. Clanchy, *From Memory to Written Record*, (Edward Arnold, London, 1979), pp. 1–3

13. H. E. Hallam, *The New Lands of Elloe* (Leicester U.P., 1954), pp. 15–16

14. J. Field, *English Field Names: A Dictionary* (David & Charles, Newton Abbot, 1972)

15. H. D. G. Foxall, *Shropshire Field Names* (Shrops. Arch. Soc., Shrewsbury, 1980)

16. PRO, E32/227

17. C. Hart. *The Verderers and Forest Laws of Dean* (David & Charles, Newton Abbot, 1971), p. 62. This book can be used as a guide to the use of medieval and later forest records

18. For further information on early maps, read Paul Hindle, *Maps for Local History* (Batsford, London, 1988), pp. 13–17

19. J. B. Harley, *Maps for the Local Historian: A Guide to the British Sources* (Nat. Council of Soc. Service, 1972), p. 27

20. Shrops. R. O., Bridgewater Colln. 212/Box 466

21. A. R. H. Baker & R. A. Butler, *Studies of Field Systems in the British Isles* (Cambridge U.P., 1973), pp. 10–16

22. Harley, *Maps for the Local Historian*, p. 20

23. Ibid., p. 26

24. A. R. H. Baker & J. B. Harley, *Man made the Land* (David & Charles, Newton Abbot, 1973), pp. 62, 65

25. J. Thirsk, 'The Content and Sources of English Agrarian History after 1500', in J. Thirsk, *The Rural Economy of England: Collected Essays* (The Hambledon Press, London, 1984), p. 5

26. The Merchant Tailors' Company, Records I, 602–16 (for 1572); IX, 113–5 (for 1624); Misc. 13/3 (for 1711); Misc. 13 (15) (for 1772); Herefs. & Worcs. R.O. (Worcester), B.A. 494, Class 899: 35 (for 1654 and 1669)

27. G. P. Mander, *The History of Wolverhampton School* (Steens, Wolverhampton, 1913), p. 455

28. Joan Wake & D. C. Webster, eds., 'The Letters of Daniel Eaton to the Third Earl of Cardigan 1725–1732', *Northants Record Society*, 24, 1971, *passim*

29. E. Kerridge, *The Agricultural Revolution* (Kelley, New York, 1968), p. 253

30. Shrops. R.O., Davenport House MSS, 2713/Box 29

31. Shrops. R.O., Corbett (Action Reynalds) Colln. 322/68

32. PRO, E315 Misc. Book 397

33. W. C. Richardson, 'Records of the Court of Augmentations', *Journal of Soc. of Archivists*, 1, 1955–9, pp. 159–68

34. S. J. Madge, *The Domesday of Crown Lands* (Routledge & Sons, London, 1938), pp. 123–32

35. Ibid., p. 175

36. Toulmin Smith, *Leland's Itinerary*, I, pp. 21–2

37. Richard Gough, *Antiquityes and Memoyres of the Parish of Myddle* (Shrewsbury, 1875), p. 33

38. J. A. Yelling, *Common Field and Enclosure in England 1450–1850* (Macmillan, London, 1977), p. 64

39. M. W. Beresford, 'Glebe Terriers and Open Field Leicestershire', in W. G. Hoskins, ed., 'Studies in Leicestershire Agrarian History', *Trans. Leics. Arch. Soc.*, 24, 1949, pp. 221–38

40. Herefs. & Worcs. R.O. (Hereford), Glebe Terriers, 13/22, Highley, 3 Feb. 1625/6

41. P. R. Edwards, '1540–1750', in G. C. Baugh, ed., *The Victoria History of Shropshire, IV, Agriculture* (Oxford U.P., 1989), pp. 119–21

42. J. S. Purvis, ed., Select XVI Century Causes in Tithe, *Yorks. Arch. Soc., Rec. Ser.*, 114 (1949), pp. 98–9

43. For a discussion of the value of the records of the Equity Courts to the Local Historian, read D. Gerhold, 'The Records of the Courts of Equity', parts 1 & 2', *The Local Historian*, 17 (7–8), 1987

44. M. W. Beresford, *The Lost Villages of England* (Lutterworth Press, London, 1954), p. 109

45. M. C. Hill, 'The Wealdmoors 1560–1660', *Trans. Shrops. Arch. Soc.*, 54, 1953, pp. 255–326; P. R. Edwards, 'Disputes

in the Weald Moors in the Late 16th. and Early 17th. Centuries,' *Trans. Shrops. Arch. Soc.*, 63, 1985, p. 1–10

46. Yelling, *op. cit.*, pp. 7–8
47. Michael Turner, *English Parliamentary Enclosure* (Dawson, Folkestone, 1980), p. 33
48. Ibid., p. 34
49. Ibid., p. 18
50. Harley, *Maps for the Local Historian*, p. 34
51. W. G. Hoskins & L. Dudley Stamp, *The Common Lands of England and Wales*, (Collins, London, 1963), pp. 89–94
52. Harley, *Maps for the Local Historian*, pp. 40–50
53. Ibid., p. 46
54. Kain & Prince, *Tithe Surveys*, pp. 70–80, 81–6
55. This section is based on J. B. Harley, *Maps for the Local Historian*, pp. 63–76
56. This section is based on *The Historian's Guide to Ordnance Survey Maps* (Nat. Council of Soc. Service, London, 1964), *passim*
57. F. G. Aldsworth, Parish Boundaries on Record, *The Local Historian*, 15 (1), 1982, pp. 34–40
58. Wolverhampton G.S. Archives, Rushock Estate Valuation 1841
59. Ibid., Land Agents' Reports
60. Shrops. R.O., War Agricultural Committee minute books, 207/1
61. Ibid., 207/10
62. David Cox, 'The County Council 1889–1974', *The Victoria History of Shropshire III* (1979), pp. 197–8
63. William Cobbett, *Rural Rides*, Everyman Library edn. (Dent, London, 1912), *passim*
64. Quoted in G. E. Mingay, *Arthur Young and his Times*, (Macmillan, London, 1975), p. 101
65. For example, William Marshall, *Marshall's Rural Economy of the West of England*, II (David & Charles, Newton Abbott Reprint 1970), *passim*
66. Shrops. R.O., 800/Box 20
67. B. Harrison, 'Researching the Medieval Landscape', in Alan Rogers, ed., *Group Projects in Local History* (Dawson, Folkstone, 1977), pp. 33–53

Chapter Five (pp. 90–110)

1. Darby, *op. cit.*, pp. 36–8

2. A. M. Everitt, *New Avenues in English Local History*, Leicester U.P., 1970), pp. 7–10

3. A. M. Everitt, 'The Marketing of Agricultural Produce', in J. Thirsk, ed., *The Agrarian History of England and Wales, IV, 1500–1640* (Cambridge U.P., 1967) (hereafter Thirsk, *Agrarian History, IV*), pp. 467–8

4. Ibid., pp. 563–89, for a discussion of the changes that occurred and the problems they created

5. Darby, *op. cit.*, p. 73

6. R. H. Britnell, 'The Proliferation of Markets in England, 1200–1349', *Econ. Hist. Review*, 2nd. ser., 39 (2), 1981, p. 211

7. P. Riden, *Record Sources for Local History*, (Batsford, London, 1987), pp. 25–7

8. Britnell, *op. cit.*, pp. 219–20. For a local example of trends, read D. M. Palliser & C. Pinnock, 'The Markets of Medieval Staffordshire', *North Staffs. Journal of Field Studies*, 11, 1971, pp. 49–63

9. Everitt, Marketing, pp. 467–9

10. Wendy Walker, *Essex Markets and Fairs* (Essex R.O., Chelmsford, 1981), p. 36

11. J. A. Chartres, 'Markets, Fairs and the Community in Seventeenth and Eighteenth Century England', *University of Leeds, School of Economic Studies, Discussion Paper Series*, no. 6, 1974, p. 5

12. William Owen, *Owen's Book of Fairs* (London, 1756 edn)

13. Edwards, *Horse Trade*, pp. 66–7

14. Palliser & Pinnock, *op. cit.*, p. 54

15. Richard Blome, *Britannia* (London, 1673), pp. 193–4

16. Daniel Defoe, *A Tour through the whole island of Great Britain*, ed. by Pat Rogers (Penguin, Hardmondsworth, 1971), p. 406

17. Edwards, *Horse Trade*, pp. 55–60

18. Ibid., pp. 172–4, list of extant toll books

19. Shrops. R.O., Shrewsbury Corporation Records, 2645–68

20. Edwards, *Horse Trade*, pp. 68–70. For an example of a local study based on toll books, read P. Edwards, 'The Horse Trade of Chester in the Sixteenth and Seventeenth Centuries', *Journal of Chester Arch. Soc.*, 62, 1979, pp. 91–106

21. E. M. Dance, ed., 'Guildford Borough Records 1514–1546', *Surrey Record Society*, 24, 1958, pp. 22–3

22. Everitt, 'Marketing', p. 581
23. M. W. Beresford, The Common Informer, the Penal Statutes and Economic Regulation, *Econ. Hist. Review*, 2nd. ser., 10 (2), 1957–8, pp. 221–38
24. Ibid., p. 221
25. Owen, *Fairs*, preface
26. B(ritish) P(arliamentary) P(apers), *Report of the Royal Commission on Market Rights* (C6268 – I to VI A) H.C. (1890–1), xxxvii–xl
27. J. Blackman, 'The Food Supply of an Industrial Town: A Study of Sheffield's Public Markets 1780–1900', *Business History*, 5 (2), 1963, p. 84. I am grateful to Dr Wendy Thwaites for this reference.
28. Wendy Thwaites, 'Dearth and the Marketing of Agricultural Produce: Oxfordshire *c*. 1750–1800', *Agric. Hist. Review*, 33 (2), 1985, p. 130
29. D. Alexander, *Retailing in England during the Industrial Revolution* (London U.P., 1970). pp. 45–7
30. Lucy Adrian, 'The Nineteenth Century Gazette Corn Returns from East Anglian Markets', *Journal of Hist. Geog.*, 3 (3), 1977, pp. 217–23. I am grateful to Dr Wendy Thwaites for this reference.
31. Wendy Thwaites, 'The Assize of Bread in 18th. Century Oxford', *Oxoniensia*, 51, 1986, pp. 171–81
32. A. M. Everitt, 'Town and Country in Victorian Leicestershire: The Role of the Village Carrier', in A. M. Everitt, ed., *Perspectives in English Urban History* (Macmilan, London, 1973), pp. 213–40
33. Rusher's *Banbury List*, 1798, 1812. Quoted in Wendy Thwaites, 'The Marketing of Agricultural Produce in 18th. Century Oxfordshire', unpub. University of Birmingham PhD dissertation, 1980, pp. 45–7, 55–6
34. Thwaites, Dearth, p. 126
35. *Jackson's Oxford Journal*, 15 Sep. 1753. Quoted in Thwaites, dissertation, p. 27
36. *Jackson's Oxford Journal*, 7 Nov. 1795. Quoted in Thwaites, dissertation, p. 251
37. Thwaites, dissertation, p. 251
38. J. Bailey & G. Culley, *General View of the Agriculture of the County of Northumberland, Cumberland and Westmorland* (1805/Frank Graham facsimile edn. Newcastle upon Tyne, 1972), p. 174
39. I am grateful to Dr Wendy Thwaites for this point.

40. Thwaites, dissertation, pp. 269, 475–6
41. J. A. Chartres, 'Marketing', in Thirsk', *Agrarian History, V.ii*, p. 417
42. P. R. Edwards, 'The Cattle Trade of Shropshire in the Late Sixteenth and Seventeenth Centuries', *Midland History*, 6, 1981, pp. 84–5
43. Edwards, Dairy Farming, pp. 185–6
44. Herefs. & Worcs. R. O. (Hereford), Foley Colln. PH/111
45. B.P.P. Report of Royal Commission on Market Rights 1888 (C5550 – II), Session 1888, vol. 54, 10267
46. Surrey R.O. 65/4/22–4
47. Richard Hillier, 'Auction Catalogues and Notices: Their Value for the Local Historian', *The Local Historian*, 13 (3), 1978. pp. 131–9
48. Shrops. R.O. Class 4752
49. Jonathan Brown, *Agriculture in England: A Survey of Farming, 1870–1947* (Manchester U.P., 1987), p.115
50. Ibid.
51. Ibid., pp. 120–1
52. N. Hicks, *Farming in the West Country* (David Rendel Ltd., London 1968), p. 44
53. Ibid., p. 40
54. B. Short, 'The Art and Craft of Chicken Cramming: Poultry in the Weald of Sussex 1850–1950', *Agric. Hist. Review*, 30 (1), 1982, p. 27
55. Everitt, 'Marketing', pp. 579–80; Act of 15 Charles II c.7
56. Chartres, 'Marketing', p. 469
57. Shrops. R.O., 254, Licensed Drovers 1613–1714
58. Edwards, *Horse Trade*, pp. 88–9
59. Ibid., p. 85
60. B. Baker, 'The Marketing of Corn in the First Half of the Eighteenth Century: North-East Kent', *Agric. Hist. Review*, 18 (2), 1970, p. 149
61. Edwards, 'Cattle trade', p. 85
62. D. Baker, *op. cit.*, p. 133

Chapter Six (pp. 115–35)

1. Miller & Hatcher, p. 15
2. Ibid., p. 16
3. Ibid., p. 173–4
4. For example, the I.P.M. taken at Pendock (Worcs.) of the lands of John de Pendock, in J. Willis Bund, ed.,

'Inquisitions .Post Mortem for Worcestershire 1242–1326', *Worcs. Hist. Soc.*, 1894, pp. 111–12

5. Miller & Hatcher, pp. 22, 116–17; E. Kerridge, *Agrarian Problems in the Sixteenth Century and After* (George Allen & Unwin, London, 1969), pp. 33–4; Mildred Campbell, *The English Yeoman* (Merlin Press, 1967), pp. 109–10

6. Mildred Campbell, *op. cit.*, pp. 110–12

7. A. L. Poole, *Oxford History of England III: From Domesday Book to Magna Carta* (Clarendon Press, Oxford, 1955), pp. 18–20

8. Miller & Hatcher, p. 23; R. Welldon Finn, *Domesday Book: A Guide* (Phillimore, Chichester, 1973), pp. 43–5; J. Z. Titov, *English Rural Society 1200–1350* (George Allen & Unwin, London, 1969), pp. 56–9

9. Miller & Hatcher, pp. 118–19

10. *Ibid.*, pp. 22–3, 116, 118; Mildred Campbell, *op. cit.*, pp. 113–15

11. Miller & Hatcher, p. 116

12. Mildred Campbell, *op. cit.*, , pp. 113–17

13. P. Riden, *Record Sources for Local History* (Batsford, London, 1987), pp. 25–6

14. N. W. Alcock, *Old Title Deeds: A Guide for Local and Family Historians* (Phillimore, Chichester, 1986), pp. 52–3

15. F. G. Emmison, Final Concords, *The Local Historian*, 14 (7), 1981, p. 415

16. W. G. Hoskins, *The Midland Peasant* (Macmillan, London, 1965), pp. 30–1

17. A. A. Dibben, *Title Deeds 13th. – 19th. Centuries*, H72 (The History Assoc., 1968), pp. 9–11

18. Riden, *Record Sources*, pp. 89–90

19. Alcock, *op. cit.*, pp. 41–6; Dibben, *op. cit.*, p. 12

20. Riden, *Record Sources*, pp. 34–5; Alcock, *op. cit.*, pp. 50–1

21. Alcock, *op. cit.*, pp. 46–7

22. Miller & Hatcher, p. 135

23. Ibid., p. 136

24. Ibid., p. 23

25. Ibid., pp. 116–17

26. Ibid., pp. 135–9

27. J. L. Bolton, *The Medieval Economy 1150–1500* (Dent, London, 1980), pp. 214–19, 236–40; W. G. Hoskins, *The Age of Plunder: England under Henry VIII 1500–1547* (Longman, London, 1976), p. 61

28. Mildred Campbell, *op. cit.*, pp. 126–9

29. This section is based on Kerridge, *Agrarian Problems*, pp. 35–41
30. C. Clay, Landlords and Estate Management in England, in Thirsk, *Agrarian History, V. ii*, p. 172
31. P. R. Edwards, 'The Farming Economy of North-East Shropshire in the Seventeenth Century', unpub. University of Oxford, D. Phil. dissertation, 1976, p. 28
32. This section is based on Kerridge, *Agrarian Problems*, pp. 43–4
33. Ibid., pp. 59–60; Mildred Campbell, *op. cit.*, pp. 149–50
34. Edwards, 'Shropshire Farming 1540–1750', pp. 137–8
35. Kerridge, *Agrarian Problems*, p. 70; Mildred Campbell, *op. cit.*, p. 133
36. Mildred Campbell, *op. cit.*, pp. 147–53
37. Edwards, Shropshire Farming 1540–1750, pp. 137–8
38. Margaret Spufford, *Contrasting Communities: English Villagers in the Sixteenth and Seventeenth Centuries*, (Cambridge U.P., 1974), p. 66
39. R. C. Russell, *The Enclosures of Alkborough 1765–1768, West Halton 1772–1773, Whitton 1773–1775, Scotter and Scotterthorpe 1808–1820* (Scunthorpe Museum and Art Gallery, 1981), p. 19
40. John Holt, *General View of the County of Lancaster* (1795/ David & Charles reprint, Newton Abbot, 1969), p. 14; J. Bailey & G. Culley, *General View of . . . Cumberland*, p. 205
41. Harvey, *Manorial Records*, p. 7
42. Titov, *Rural Society*, pp. 44–5
43. Miller & Hatcher, pp. 45–6
44. R. Welldon Finn, *Domesday Book: A Guide* (Phillimore. Chichester, 1973), pp. 78–9
45. R. Lennard, *Rural England 1086–1135: A Study of Social and Agrarian Conditions* (Clarendon Press, Oxford, 1959), p. 372; Miller & Hatcher, p. 118
46. Miller & Hatcher, p. 120
47. R. H. Hilton, *A Medieval Society: The West Midlands at the End of the Thirteenth Century* (Cambridge U.P., 1983), p. 153
48. Titov, *Rural Society*, pp. 139–43
49. Miller & Hatcher, p. 206
50. Harvey, *Manorial Records*, p. 23
51. E. Toms, ed., Chertsey Abbey Court Rolls Abstract, *Surrey Record Society*, 21, 1954, pp. 111–12

52. Miller & Hatcher, pp. 137–9, 142–3
53. Ibid., p. 146
54. G. C. Homans, *English Villagers of the Thirteenth Century* (Harper & Row, New York, 1970), p. 202
55. Spufford, *Contrasting Communities*, p. 101
56. M. K. McIntosh, 'Land, Tenure and Population on the Royal Manor of Havering, Essex', *Econ. Hist. Review*, 2nd ser., 33 (1), 1980, pp. 17–31
57. C. Howell, *Land, Family and Inheritance in Transition: Kibworth Harcourt 1280–1700* (Cambridge U.P., 1983), pp. 19–24
58. C. Clay, 'Lifeleasehold in the Western Counties of England 1650–1750', *Agric. Hist. Review*, 29 (2), 1981, pp. 93–4
59. Ibid., pp. 91–2
60. Staffs. R.O., Sutherland Colln. D593/I/1/4
61. Clay, Lifeleasehold, pp. 83–4, 86
62. Kerridge, *Agrarian Problems*, pp. 45–8; Clay, Landlords, pp. 208–14
63. Chambers & Mingay, pp. 46–8
64. *Report of the Select Committee on Agricultural Customs*, BPP 1847–8, vol. VII. Quoted in P. Horn, *The Rural World 1780–1850: Social Change in the English Countryside* (Hutchinson, London, 1980), p. 239
65. Chambers & Mingay, pp. 164–6
66. Horn, *The Rural World*, pp. 239–40
67. Peter Roebuck, 'Leases and Tenancy Agreements', *The Local Historian*, 10 (1), 1972, pp. 7–11
68. Howell, *Kibworth Harcourt*, p. 62
69. Shrops. R.O., Kilmorrey of Shavington Colln. 946/B 640
70. C. J. Harrison, 'Village Surveys: A Comment', *Agric. Hist. Review*, 27 (2), 1979, pp. 82–9
71. Shrops. R.O., Bridgewater Colln. Box 346/24
72. Peter Finch, 'Land Holding and Sub-Letting: A Surrey Manor in 1613', *The Local Historian*, 18 (1), 1988, pp. 16–18
73. Staffs. R.O., Bradford Colln. D1287/18/15, John Bridgeman's Letter Book, 14 May 1740
74. Lambeth Palace Library, VH 96/2248, Probate Will of Thomas Saunders of Putney, Surrey, proved 3 Feb. 1614
75. Heref. & Worcs. R.O. (Hereford), Probate Will of Thomas Walworth of Hopton in the Hole, Stanton Lacy,

proved 27 Jan. 1707/8; ibid., Probate Will of James Smith of Overton, Richard's Castle (Shrops.), proved 10 June 1667

76. Charles Vancouver, *General View of the Agriculture of the County of Devon* (1808/David & Charles reprint, Newton Abbot, 1969), pp. 81–2; John Holt, *General View of Lancashire*, p. 14; Arthur Young, *General View of the County of Sussex* (1813/David & Charles reprint, Newton Abbot, 1970), p. 43

Chapter Seven (pp. 136–54)

1. Dyer, *Lords and Peasants*, p. 110
2. Miller & Hatcher, p. 220
3. Finberg, 'Anglo-Saxon England', pp. 511–2
4. Miller & Hatcher, pp. 121–8
5. For example, the extent of the manor of Littleton (Hants.), 1265–6, printed in Titov, *Rural Society*, pp. 145–50
6. Harley, 'The Hundred Rolls', *The Amateur Historian*, 5 (1), 1961, pp. 11–13
7. Miller & Hatcher, pp. 122–4
8. Ibid., pp. 125–7
9. Hilton, *A Medieval Society*, pp. 135–6
10. Ibid., p. 136
11. Miller & Hatcher, p. 125
12. Ibid., p. 219
13. Titov, *Rural Society*, p. 129; L. F. Salzman, ed., 'Ministers' Accounts of the Manor of Petworth 1347–1353', *Sussex Record Society*, 55, 1955, pp. 14–15
14. Miller & Hatcher, p. 220
15. Salzman, Petworth Accounts, pp. 5–8
16. S. A. C. Penn, 'Female Wage-Earners in Late Fourteenth-Century England', *Agric. Hist. Review*, 35 (1), 1987, p. 2
17. Ibid., pp. 3–11
18. Shrops. R. O., More of Linley Colln. 1037/11/5
19. Ibid., class 1037/9
20. Ann Kussmaul, *Servants in Husbandry in Early Modern England*, (Cambridge U.P., 1981), pp. 84–9
21. Ibid., pp. 11–16
22. Lincs. A. O., SWINDERBY PAR 23/1
23. Kussmaul, *Servants in Husbandry*, pp. 78–85
24. R. W. Malcolmson, *Life and Labour in England 1700–1780* (Hutchinson, London, 1981), pp. 37–8

25. C. W. Chalklin, *Seventeenth Century Kent* (Longman, London, 1965), p. 249
26. P. Brassley, A. Lambert & P. Saunders, eds., Accounts of the Reverend John Crakanthorp of Fowlmere 1682–1710, *Cambs. Rec. Soc.* 8, 1988, p. 154
27. Staffs. R.O., Bradford Colln. temp. ref. F/590
28. Surrey R.O., Howard Colln. 63/1/97, Earl of Effingham's Receipt Book for Day Labourers' Wages 1744–5
29. Kussmaul, *Servants in Husbandry*, pp. 36–7
30. Wake & Webster, 'Letters of Daniel Eaton', *passim*
31. Donald Woodward, *The Farming and Memoranda Books of Henry Best of Elmswell 1642*, (British Academy, 1984), pp. xxxix–xli, 121–2 and *passim*
32. C. P. Trimmer, 'The Turnip, the New Husbandry and the English Agricultural Revolution', *Quarterly Journal of Economics*, 83, 1969, pp. 385–6
33. Alan Rogers, *Approaches to Local History* (Longman, London, 1977), pp. 87–8
34. Alun Howkins, 'In the Sweat of thy Face: The Labourer and Work', in G. E. Mingay, ed., *The Victorian Countryside* (R.K.P., London, 1981), II, p. 506
35. George Ewart Evans, *Horse Power and Magic* (Faber & Faber, London, 1979), p. 184
36. Celia Miller, ed., 'The Account Books of Thomas Smith, Ireley Farm, Hailes, Gloucestershire 1865–71', *Bristol & Gloucs. Arch. Soc., Record Ser.*, 1985, pp. xxxii–xxxiii, xxxvii and *passim*
37. P. Horn, *Labouring Life in the Victorian Countryside* (Alan Sutton, Gloucestershire, 1987), pp. 69–70
38. Raphael Samuel, ed., *Village Life and Labour* (R.K.P., London, 1975), p.97
39. BBP, *Reports of Ass. Poor Law Commissioners on Emp. of Women and Children in Agric.* (510), H.C. (1843) xvii; (4202 and 4202–I), H.C. (1868–9) xiii
40. BPP, *Reports of Royal Comm. on Child Emp.* (3170), H.C. (1863) xviii; (3414, 3414–I) H.C. (1864) xxii; (3548), H.C. (1865) xx; (3678), H.C. (1866) xxiv; (3796), H.C. (1867) xvi
41. Samuel, *Village Life*, pp. 98–112
42. Horn, *Labouring Life*, pp. 84–5
43. Ibid., p. 69
44. Celia Miller, 'The Hidden Workforce: Female Workers in

Gloucestershire 1870–1901', *Southern History*, 6, 1984, pp. 139–55

45. Horn, *Labouring Life*, p. 80
46. Samuel, *Village Life*, p. 82
47. S. MacDonald, 'The Diffusion of Knowledge among Northumberland Farmers, 1780–1815', *Agric. Hist. Review*, 27 (1), 1979, p. 36
48. E. J. T. Collins, 'Migrant Labour in British Agriculture in the Nineteenth Century', *Econ. Hist. Review*, 2nd. ser., 29 (1), 1976, p. 41
49. BPP, *Report of Royal Comm. on Poor Law*, H.C. 44 (1834) xxvii–xxxviii
50. Collins, Migrant Labour, p. 50, f.n. 2
51. Ibid., pp. 50–1
52. Howkins, 'The Labourer and Work', pp. 508–9; Samuel, *Village Life*, pp. 10–11
53. Alistair Mutch, *Rural Life in South-West Lancashire 1840–1814* (Centre for North-West Regional Studies, Univ. Of Lanc., 1988), p. 33
54. Howkins, 'The Labourer and Work', p. 509
55. Horn, *Labouring Life*, pp. 73–5
56. This section is based on Peter Dewey's book, *British Agriculture in the First World War*, chaps. 4 & 9
57. Ibid., pp. 113–20
58. Ibid., pp. 120–7
59. Ibid., pp. 127–36
60. Ibid., pp. 136–7
61. Ibid., p. 48
62. Shrops. R.O., 207/1
63. Board of Agriculture, *Report of Wages and Conditions of Emp. in Agric.* (1919) Cmd. 24 & 25, BPP, 1919, viii, 37
64. Ibid., para. 123
65. Horn, *Labouring Life*, pp. 118–19
66. BPP, *Report of Sel. Comm. on Labourers' Wages*, H.C. 392 (1824) vi; *Return of Agric. Labourers' Average Weekly Earnings*, H.C. 14, 14–I, 14–II (1861) I; H.C. 371 (1868–9) 1; H.C. 181 (1871) lvi; H.C. 358 (1873) liii (Returns for Poor Law Unions); *1st & 2nd. Reports of the Board of Trade on Agric. Labourers' Wages*, H.C. (1900) lxxxii; H.C. (1905) xcvii
67. P. Horn, 'Labour Organization', in G. E. Mingay, *The Victorian Countryside*, II, pp. 580–2
68. Ibid., pp. 582–6

69. Horn, *Labouring Life*, p. 132
70. Ibid., p. 134–5
71. Ibid., p. 126
72. Ibid., pp. 127, 129
73. Ibid., p. 135

Chapter Eight (pp. 155–72)

1. John Langdon, *Horses, Oxen and Technological Innovation: The Use of Draught Animals in English Farming from 1066–1500* (Cambridge U.P. 1986), p. 128
2. Ibid., p. 130
3. Ibid., pp. 132–41
4. Ibid., pp. 142–56
5. This section is based on Langdon, *Draught Animals*, pp. 100–15
6. Salzman, Petworth Accounts, pp. 9–10
7. Hollings, 'The Red Book of Worcester', pp. 61–2
8. For example, the manor of Downton (Wilts.) 1324–5, in Titov, *Rural Society*, pp. 126–7
9. Welldon Finn, *Domesday Book*, pp. 60–1
10. Langdon, *Draught Animals*, p. 176
11. R. K. Field, 'Worcestershire Peasant Buildings: Household Goods and Farming Equipment in the Later Middle Ages', *Medieval Archaeology*, 9, 1965, pp. 137–45
12. Hilton, *A Medieval Society*, p. 104
13. Langdon, *Draught Animals*, p. 221
14. Ibid.
15. Ibid., pp. 194–5
16. Kerridge, *The Agricultural Revolution*, p. 33
17. F. W. Steer, *Farm and Cottage Inventories of Mid-Essex 1635–1749* (Phillimore, Chichester, 1969), pp. 217–19
18. Ibid., p. 114
19. Joan Thirsk, 'Farming Techniques', in Thirsk, *Agrarian History, IV*, pp. 163–4
20. Edwards, *Horse Trade*, pp. 5–6
21. Edwards, Shropshire Farming 1540–1750, pp. 148–9
22. Edwards, *Horse Trade*, pp. 10–13
23. Ibid., pp. 38–46
24. Ibid., p. 6
25. Brassley *et al.* Crakanthorp's Accounts, p. 181
26. Woodward, *Henry Best*, pp. 49, 105
27. Hoskins, *Local History in England*, p. 133

28. E. J. T. Collins, 'The Rationality of "Surplus" Agricultural Labour: Mechanization in English Agriculture in the Nineteenth Century', *Agric. Hist. Review*, 35 (1) 1987, p. 39
29. Chambers & Mingay, p. 69
30. Ibid., pp. 69–70
31. E. J. T. Collins, 'The Age of Machinery', in Mingay, *The Victorian Countryside*, p. 205
32. Alistair Mutch, the Mechanization of the Harvest in South-West Lancashire, 1850–1914, *Agric. Hist. Review*, 29 (2), 1981, pp. 126–8
33. Ibid., p. 128
34. W. A. Armstrong, 'The Flight from the Land', in Mingay, *The Victorian Countryside* (R.K.P., London, 1981), p. 120
35. T. C. Barker, 'The Delayed Decline of the Horse in the Twentieth Century', in F. M. L. Thompson, ed., *Horses in European Economic History: A Preliminary Canter* (Brit. Agric. Hist. Soc., Reading, 1983), p. 109
36. E. J. Hobsbawm & G. Rude, *Captain Swing* (Lawrence & Wishart, 1969), passim
37. Ibid., pp. 198–207
38. Ibid., pp. 253–64
39. Collins, 'Mechanization', p. 37
40. Ibid., p. 40
41. Collins, 'Migrant Labour', p. 57
42. Jonathan Brown, *Agriculture in England: A Study of Farming, 1870–1947* (Manchester U.P., 1987), pp. 25–6
43. Mutch, Mechanization, p. 131
44. Ibid., pp. 31–2
45. Parker, *Coke of Norfolk*, p. 172
46. Mutch, 'Mechanization', p. 128
47. J. R. Wordie, *Estate Management in 18th. Century England*, (Royal. Hist. Soc., London, 1982), pp. 208–11
48. S. MacDonald, 'The Progress of the Early Threshing Machine', *Agric. Hist. Review*, 23 (1), 1975, pp. 63–77
49. Shrops. R.O., 4752/1/31
50. Mutch, Mechanization, pp. 126–32
51. John Sheail, 'Land Improvement and Reclamation: The Experiences of the First World War in England and Wales', *Agric. Hist. Review*, 24 (2), 1976, pp. 112–13
52. Ibid., p. 113
53. Keith Chivers, *The Shire Horse* (J. A. Allen, London, 1976), pp. 741–52

54. Sheail, Land Improvement, pp. 114–18
55. Ibid., p. 115–17
56. Shrops. R.O., 207/1, W.A.E.C. Minute Book, 22 May 1917
57. Roy Brigden, Victorian Farms, (The Crowood Press, Ramsbury, 1986), p.23
58. Ibid., p. 58
59. S. W. Martins, 'The Farm Buildings of the Agricultural Revolution', *The Local Historian*, 12 (7), 1977, p. 414
60. Wolverhampton G.S. Archives, Land Agents' Reports, 22 Jan. 1870
61. M. W. Beresford, 'Building History from Fire Insurance Records', *Urban History Yearbook*, 1976, pp. 7–14; L. M. Wulcko, 'Fire Insurance Policies as a Source of Local History', *The Local Historian*, 9 (1), 1970, pp. 3–8

FURTHER READING

Chapter One

B. M. S. Campbell, *The Geography of Seigneurial Agriculture in Medieval England* (Cambridge U.P., forthcoming)

B. M. S. Campbell, Agricultural Progress in Medieval England: Some Evidence from Eastern Norfolk, *Econ. Hist. Review*, 2nd. ser., 36 (1), 1983

H. C. Darby, ed., *A New Historical Geography of England before 1600* (Cambridge U.P., 1976)

C. C. Dyer, *Lords and Peasants in a Changing Society* (Cambridge U.P., 1980)

R. Welldon Finn, *Domesday Book: A Guide* (Phillimore,, Chichester, 1973)

P. D. A. Harvey, *Manorial Records*, Archives and the User, no. 5 (British Records Assoc., 1984)

E. Kerridge, The Manorial Survey at an Historical Source, *The Amateur Historian*, 7 (1), 1966

Chapter Two

J. V. Beckett, *The Agricultural Revolution* (Basil Blackwell, Oxford, 1990)

E. Kerridge, *The Agricultural Revolution* (Kelley, New York, 1967)

Margaret Spufford, Probate Inventories as a Source: A Critical View, in John Chartres & David Hey, eds., *English Rural Society 1500–1800: Essays in Honour of Joan Thirsk* (Cambridge U.P., 1990)

Joan Thirsk, The Content and Sources of English Agrarian History after 1500, *Agric. Hist. Review*, 3 (2), 1955

Joan Thirsk, ed., *The Agrarian History of England and Wales, IV, 1500–1640*, (Cambridge U.P., 1967) and *V, 1640–1750* (Cambridge U.P., 1985)

Joan Thirsk, Seventeenth Century Agriculture and Social Change, in Joan Thirsk, ed., *Land, Church and People* (British Agric. History Society, Reading, 1970)

Chapter Three

Jonathan Brown, *Agricultural in England: A Survey of Farming 1870–1947* (Manchester U.P., 1987)

J. D. Chambers & G. E. Mingay, *The Agricultural Revolution* (Batsford, London, 1966)

P. E. Dewey, *British Agriculture in the First World War* (Routledge, London, 1989)

G. E. Mingay, ed., *The Agrarian History of England and Wales, VI, 1750–1850* (Cambridge U.P., 1989)

P. J. Perry, *British Agriculture 1875–1914* (Methuen, London, 1973)

Chapter Four

M. Aston, *Interpreting the Landscape: Landscape Archaeology in Local Studies* (Batsford, London, 1985)

A. R. H. Baker & J. B. Harley, eds., *Man Made the Land* (David & Charles, Newton Abbot, 1973)

Paul Hindle, *Maps for Local History* (Batsford, London, 1988)

W. G. Hoskins, *The Making of the English Landscape* (Hodder & Stoughton, London, 1955)

W. G. Hoskins, *Fieldwork in Local History* (Faber & Faber, London, 1967)

R. J. P. Kain & H. C. Prince, *The Tithe Surveys of England and Wales* (Cambridge U.P., 1985)

Oliver Rackham, *The History of the Countryside* (Dent, London, 1986)

A. Rogers & T. Rowley, eds., *Landscapes and Documents* (Nat. Council of Social Service, London, 1974)

C. C. Taylor, *Fields in the English Landscape* (Alan Sutton, Gloucester, 1987)

The Historian's Guide to Ordnance Survey Maps (Nat. Council of Social Service, London, 1964)

M. Turner, *English Parliamentary Enclosure* (Dawson, Folkstone, 1980)

Chapter Five

D. Alexander, *Retailing in England during the Industrial Revolution* (Athlone Press, London, 1970)

B. L. Anderson & A. J. H. Latham, *The Market in History*, (Croom Helm, Beckenham, Kent, 1986)

R. H. Britnell, The Proliferation of Markets in England 1200–1349, *Econ. Hist. Review*, 2nd. ser., 34 (2), 1981

J. Brown, *The English Market Town: A Social and Economic History 1750–1914* (Crowood Press, Ramsbury, 1986)

J. A. Chartres, Internal Trade in England 1500–1700 (Macmillan, London, 1977)

J. A. Chartres, The Marketing of Agricultural Produce, in Joan Thirsk, ed., *The Agrarian History of England and Wales, V.ii, 1640–1750* (Cambridge U.P., 1985)

P. Edwards, *The Horse Trade of Tudor and Stuart England* (Cambridge U.P., 1988)

A. M. Everitt, The Marketing of Agricultural Produce, in Joan Thirsk, ed., *The Agrarian History of England and Wales, IV, 1500–1640* (Cambridge U.P., 1967)

A. M. Everitt, *New Avenues in Local History* (Leicester U.P., 1970)

D. G. Hey, *Packmen, Carriers and Packhorse Roads: Trade and Communications in North Derbyshire and South Yorkshire* (Leicester U.P., 1980)

R. Perren, Markets and Marketing, in G. E. Mingay, ed., *The Agrarian History of England and Wales, VI, 1750–1850* (Cambridge U.P., 1989)

Chapter Six

N. W. Alcock, *Old Title Deeds: A Guide for Local and Family Historians* (Phillimore, Chichester, 1986)

M. T. Clanchy, *From Memory to Written Record* (Edward Arnold, London, 1979)

C. Clay, Landlords and Estate Management in England, in Joan Thirsk, ed., *The Agrarian History of England and Wales, V.ii. 1640–1750* (Cambridge U.P., 1985)

Jack Goody, Joan Thirsk & E. P. Thompson, eds., *Family and Inheritance: Rural Society in Western Europe 1200–1800* (Cambridge U.P., 1976)

C. J. Harrison, Elizabethan Village Surveys: A Comment, *Agric. Hist. Review*, 27 (2), 1979

E. Kerridge, *Agrarian Problems in the Sixteenth Century and After* (George Allen & Unwin, London, 1969)

Peter Roebuck, Leases and Tenancy Agreements, *The Local Historian*, 10 (1), 1972

J. Z. Titow, *English Rural Society 1200–1350* (George Allen & Unwin, London, 1969)

Chapter Seven

A. Armstrong, *Farmworkers: A Social and Economic History 1770–1980*, (Batsford, London 1988)

E. J. T. Collins, Migrant Labour in British Agriculture in the Nineteenth Century, *Econ. Hist. Review*, 2nd. ser., 29 (1), 1976

F. G. Davenport, The Decay of Villeinage in East Anglia, *Trans. Royal. Hist. Soc.*, N.S., 14 (1900)

A. M. Everitt, Farm Labourers, in Joan Thirsk, ed., *The Agrarian History of England and Wales, IV, 1500–1640* (Cambridge U.P., 1967)

Pamela Horn, *The Rural World 1780–1850* (Hutchinson, London, 1980)

Pamela Horn, *Labouring Life in the Victorian Countryside* (Alan Sutton, Gloucester, 1987)

E. A. Kominsky, Services and Money Rents in the Thirteenth Century, *Econ. Hist. Review*, 5 (2), 1935

Ann Kussmaul, *Servants in Husbandry in Early Modern England* (Cambridge U.P., 1981)

R. W. Malcolmson, *Life and Labour in England 1700–1780* (Hutchinson, London, 1981)

M. M. Postan, Chronology of Labour Services, in M. E. Minchinton, ed., *Essays in Agrarian History* (David & Charles, Newton Abbot, 1968), I.

Chapter Eight

E. J. Collins, the Age of Machinery, in G. E. Mingay, ed., *The Victorian Countryside*, I (R.K.P., London, 1981)

E. J. T. Collins, The Rationality of 'Surplus' Agricultural Labour: Mechanization in English Agriculture in the Nineteenth Century, *Agric. Hist. Review*, 35 (1), 1987

G. E. Fussell, *The Farmer's Tools: The History of British Farm Implements, Tools and Machinery AD 1500–1900* (Orbis Publishing, London, 1981)

J. Langdon, *Horses, Oxen and Technological Innovation: The Use of Draught Animals in English Farming from 1066–1500* (Cambridge U.P., 1986)

J. Langdon, Agricultural Equipment, in G. Astill & A. Grant, eds., *The Countryside and Medieval England*, (Basil Blackwell, Oxford, 1988)

S. Porter, Farm Transport in Huntingdonshire, 1610–1749, *Journal of Transport History*, 3rd. ser., 3 (1), 1982

Lynn White junr., *Medieval Technology and Social Change* (Oxford U.P., 1962)

INDEX